Planet Earth
- We Have a Problem

Feedback Dynamics and the Acceleration of Climate Change

*Proceedings of a briefing given in the House of Commons, London
to the All Party Parliamentary Climate Change Group (APPCCG)
on the 6th June 2007*

Peter Cox, Deepak Rughani, Peter Wadhams, David Wasdell
Foreword by Colin Challen MP

Published by the APPCCG in association with the Meridian Programme
2007

Published by the All Party Parliamentary Climate Change Group
in association with the Meridian Programme

c/o Colin Challen MP
House of Commons
London
SW1A 0AA

Printed by
Angus Print Ltd
Domestic Street Industrial Estate
Leeds

November, 2007

CONTENTS

Foreword

Colin Challen MP

We are getting used to the injunction that we have around 15 years left to address the problem of climate change. It feels like we still have a comfort zone in which we can fine-tune our response, get everybody on board, check that our body-politic is ship-shape and to coin a phrase 'is fit for purpose.'

Sadly, a mounting body of evidence suggests otherwise. This was the subject of an important meeting of an All Party Parliamentary Climate Change Group meeting in June, 2007, which heard about positive feedbacks and carbon sink failures - the dynamics of accelerated climate change. The meeting took place against the background of the publication of reports from the Intergovernmental Panel on Climate Change (IPCC) cataloguing the carefully peer reviewed and very firm evidence that the cause of climate change is anthropogenic and is every bit as serious as we fear.

The IPCC reports have a time lag - due to a rigorous scrutiny of the evidence which can safely be included in the Summary for Policy Makers - and this means that detailed IPCC consideration of some of the issues covered in this publication has yet to undergo full assessment. The IPCC have a system for making their assessments which categorise the level of certainty each of their various conclusions can reasonably assume. In the case of positive feedbacks and sink failures, there is still much more scientific exploration required. But let us not be in any doubt that it is not whether such dynamics occur, it is more a question of being unsure as to their scale, timing and perhaps location that needs a greater understanding.

It is my view that a lack of certainty on the latter issues should not deter us from factoring in the dangers posed by feedback dynamics. We urgently need to better understand how they may accelerate climate change. We cannot rely purely on estimating anthropogenic-related climate change and dealing with that in isolation. As is made clear in this book, anthropogenic greenhouse gas emissions currently act as a multiplier for the other effects, but at some point in the future our emissions may make the least significant contribution to rapid, runaway climate change.

Is this a counsel of despair? I don't think so - but it does mean having to drastically adjust our current rather sanguine approach to the politics, as represented by the Kyoto process. This approach has been characterised by the Tyndall Centre for Climate Change Research as a 'race to be second,' meaning that no country appears *really* willing to take the lead although all have something to say, usually about their vested interests.

It is 15 years since the Earth Summit in Rio and apparently we have another 15 years to solve the problem, by which is meant passing the peak in global greenhouse gas emissions and delivering a sharp decline. The first phase of the Kyoto protocol will not deliver this, and that agreement does not expire until 2012 - five years into this crucial decade and a half. In those five years, the emissions from rapidly developing countries will have increased dramatically, and if recent experience is anything to go by, the emissions from the developed world will not have declined. Indeed, developed world emissions have continued to rise, albeit at a slower rate.

Perhaps the higher profile we give to feedback dynamics will encourage a more urgent global search for a climate change framework that is actually designed to solve the problem faster than we're creating it. Increasingly, I believe it is only a sense of alarm that will shift the politics. But for 'alarm' do not read 'panic.' It is the responsibility of leaders everywhere to fully understand the problem if they are to meet the challenge. The correct response to this alarming problem is to do all we can to make our endeavours match it. I am reminded of a caption under a picture of a Second World War American shipyard which said "We knew we would win the Battle of the Atlantic when we could build more ships than the U-boats could sink." It's time we had that spirit now.

I would like to thank the contributors, Peter Cox, Deepak Rughani, Peter Wadhams and especially David Wasdell, who has worked tirelessly to not only facilitate the original meeting but who also made this record of it possible.

Finally, as this is a record of a meeting, this affects the style - we have exercised only a light editorial touch, so very often the grammar is more of the spoken variety than the written. Most of the illustrations are as presented at the meeting, but some have been altered to better suit a printed format.

Summary for Policy Makers

David Wasdell

Introduction

This Summary for Policy Makers was written in Madrid during the Annual Meeting of the Club of Rome. It was completed on the eve of the Special Meeting of Heads of State convened in New York by the General Secretary of the United Nations to address the current crisis of Climate Change and to attempt to overcome some of the difficulties besetting the process of International negotiations prior to the meeting to be held in Bali in December 2007.

Background: The Provision of Information

Effective policy-making in the rapidly developing field of climate change depends on the continuous provision of the best available scientific analysis. By their very nature, the Assessment Reports of the Inter-Governmental Panel on Climate Change are not only scientifically conservative and constrained by what is politically and economically acceptable, they are also some two years out of date when published.

Information handling in the national and international decision-making process inevitably adds another layer of inertia. As a result, negotiating processes, strategic policies, target-setting, eventual legislation and binding treaties, are based on information and problem-definition that can be as much as ten years adrift from current reality. "Solutions" offered are to problems that no longer reflect our best understanding of the contemporary situation.

At best the response is harmlessly anachronistic. In today's context of accelerating change and deepening crisis, the outcome is dangerously dysfunctional. It locks us in to a course of action that makes the underlying problem worse, delays the emergence of effective solutions, and lulls us all into a false sense of security. It reinforces the illusion that "everything is now under control and no further initiatives are required". Nothing could be further from the truth.

The Need for a Scientific Update

In addition to the delays built in to the information-handling process, two further factors underscored the urgent need for a scientific update.

The first imperative stems from observation

Monitoring of the effects of global warming in virtually every parameter now shows a rate of acceleration that is outside the range of the ensemble of climate models underlying the IPCC 4th Assessment Report. The acceleration can be seen in:

- The rate of thinning of Arctic ice, and consequent predictions of the date of an ice-free North Pole.

- Decrease in reflection of solar energy from the shrinking snow and ice cover, with resultant increase in the rate of global warming.

- Intensification of drought conditions in Sub-Saharan Africa, North Mediterranean areas of Europe, Eastern Australia, etc.

- Increase in the melt-rate of the Greenland ice-cap, evidence of surface-melt in areas of the Antarctic ice cap, rapidation in retreat of glaciers around the world, with implications for the acceleration of sea-level rise.

- Increased intensity of rainfall events with consequent flooding.

- Slow-down in the Gulf Stream (the thermo-haline circulation) with far-reaching consequential changes in the climate.

- Increased energy, wind-speed and damage in tropical storms whether in the typhoons and cyclones of the Pacific or the hurricanes of the Atlantic.

- Increase in speed of up-ward and pole-ward migration of insect species.

- Increased rate of extinction of species of fauna and flora in vulnerable habitats around the world.

- Acceleration in the rate of drying, die-back, burning, and carbon-release from tropical forests.

- Degrade (some of it caused by accelerating de-forestation) in the effective capacity of the carbon-sinks whether in the oceans or in the land-based vegetation, so increasing the pace of accumulation of greenhouse gases in the atmosphere.

- Increased rate of thawing of Tundra permafrost and acceleration in release of methane.

- Start of release of methane from the vast stores of ocean-floor "clathrates" far earlier than predicted.

- Changes in monsoon activity and in the timing and availability of melt-water from mountain glaciers affecting provision for irrigation, drinking water and food production for major sectors of the human population.

It is important to note that these observed impacts of climate change are the current effects of a rise of only 0.73°C in average global temperature. It is pretty certain that we are already "locked in" to at least three times that increase as the effects of greenhouse gases already emitted slowly work their way through the system.

It is these observations that underlie the recent warning from the chief scientist of one of NASA's research centres that: **"Warming is accelerating GREATLY, especially 'recently'".**

The second imperative stems from major advance in our understanding of Climate Dynamics.

Over the last two years there has been a profound shift in the scientific understanding of the behaviour of the earth's climate system. Although some specific feedback mechanisms were included in some of the more advanced climate models, the analysis of climate dynamics as a whole has proceeded far beyond that portrayed in the latest IPCC Assessment Report. It was not taken into consideration in the Stern Report, in the formulation of the Climate Bill currently before the UK Parliament, or in the process of target-setting of the present round of International negotiations.

The outdated position of classical climate science is epitomised in a recent statement by Professor John Marburger, Chief Scientific Advisor to the White House:

"The climate is sensitive to these CO_2 emissions and as they increase, the anthropogenic contribution to global warming and climate change will simply progress. The CO_2.accumulates in the atmosphere and there is no end point. It just gets hotter and hotter, so at some point the planet becomes unliveable."

The implication is that we can, at any point, reduce the rate of emissions, stabilise the concentration, and prevent the temperature from rising any further. From this perspective, climate change is seen in terms of simple cause and effect. The choice and timing of intervention point and eventual temperature increase are ours. They will be determined by technology, economics and the level of climate impact we are prepared to tolerate and to which we feel able to adapt.

In contrast, the best modern understanding draws on insights from the discipline of systems dynamics. It is well represented by the following quote from a recent paper co-authored by a team led by Professor James Hansen, Director of NASA's Goddard Institute for Space Studies:

"The Earth's climate is remarkably sensitive to global forcings. Positive (amplifying) feedbacks predominate. This allows the entire planet to be whipsawed between climate states. Recent greenhouse gas emissions place the Earth perilously close to dramatic climate change that could run out of our control."

Here it is recognised that anthropogenic emissions act as a trigger to a complex set of mutually reinforcing feedbacks, many of them activated by rising temperature. The resultant climate change is out of all proportion to the precipitating event.

The implication is that climate change is non-linear. Once set in motion it is acceleratingly self-perpetuating. There is then only a small time-window within which human intervention has any (rapidly diminishing) chance of halting the process and returning the system to a stable state. Failure to act effectively within that window of opportunity would inevitably precipitate cataclysmic change on a par with the five mass extinction events known to have obliterated almost all life on earth.

The Briefing in Brief

In this section you will find a summary of the main points of the Briefing, presentation by presentation. The aim is to provide an appetiser before you explore the main course itself.

Presentation 1: An Introduction to Climate Dynamics

There is normally a dynamic balance between the solar energy received by planet earth and energy radiated back out into space. Since the start of the industrial revolution human emissions of "greenhouse gasses" have increasingly disturbed that balance. Less energy now escapes back to space. The difference (known technically as "radiative forcing") drives global warming.

The gap between energy received and the energy radiated is widening faster and faster, accelerated in part by continued increase in the rate of emissions, and now also by powerful feedback mechanisms inherent in the earth system itself.

In the second part of the presentation, focus shifts from the global level of energy dynamics to the specific drivers of global warming and the detail of the feedback mechanisms involved.

- Seven factors govern the change in radiative forcing:
- Atmospheric concentration of carbon-dioxide
- Atmospheric concentration of methane
- Atmospheric concentration of other greenhouse gasses
- Atmospheric concentration of water vapour
- Dust and contrails in the atmosphere
- Reflectivity of the earth surface (the "albedo effect")
- Behaviour of clouds

Associated with these drivers, six categories of feedback mechanism have been identified, most of them triggered into action as temperature starts to rise. The presentation outlines them in detail. The most powerful amplifiers of global warming are:

- Degrade of the carbon sinks
- Release of non-anthropogenic CO_2
- Discharge of methane from tundra and sea-bed deposits
- Decreased albedo as areas and duration of snow and ice reduce
- Temperature driven increase in the atmospheric concentration of water vapour

The greater the radiative forcing, (the bigger the gap between solar energy received and energy re-radiated from the earth), the faster the temperature rises. The rate of global warming is also governed by the "**thermal inertia**" of the

earth. The excess energy has to heat the air and land as well as ocean and ice. It is also absorbed by melting of ice and evaporation of water. There is therefore a major time lag in the system between the rate of radiative forcing and the resulting rise in temperature. That is why basing policies on observed effects of the current small increase in temperature is so fundamentally inappropriate.
There is one final feedback category associated with thermal inertia. The hotter it gets, the lower the inertia of the system, and the faster temperature rises.

That introductory overview of climate dynamics sets the scene for the next three presentations which provide an in-depth account of a selection of the more powerful feedback mechanisms now accelerating climate change.

Presentation 2: Feedback Dynamics of the Carbon Cycle

The feedback between physical climate change and the uptake of CO_2 by ocean and land (the degrade of carbon sinks), is especially important for two reasons:

Firstly, climate change with a given amount of emissions could be faster than previously thought.

Secondly, it has an impact on how much we have to reduce emissions in order to stabilise CO_2 concentration at any particular level.

About half of our CO_2 emissions are currently absorbed by soil and vegetation on land and by plankton and water in the oceans. Climate change could well suppress this sink. Most climate models on which the IPCC Reports depend still take no account of this carbon-cycle feedback.

We know that rising temperature decreases the amount of CO_2 that is absorbed in water. Hot surface water is lighter, so there is also less mixing of the CO_2-rich solution into the ocean depths. These feedbacks reduce the extent to which the natural sinks take up our emissions. The degrade of land-based sinks is even more pronounced. As temperatures rise and CO_2 concentrations increase, land-based sinks reverse and become a source of (non-anthropogenic) emission, so accelerating climate change. When you add in the effects of accelerating deforestation and climate-driven die-back of the Amazonian and other forest areas, the feedback intensifies.

If we take these feedbacks into account, then the "business as usual" scenario would lead to a concentration of about 1,000 parts per million of atmospheric CO_2 by the end of the century, instead of the 750ppm previously predicted. The models now attempting to take account of the carbon-cycle feedbacks have a range of results, so there is some uncertainty about the exact figures involved. But however you look at it, this is a very serious amplification of climate change.

The carbon cycle feedbacks make it harder to stabilise concentration of atmospheric CO_2. We have to start reducing emissions more quickly, cuts have to be deeper, and, because the sinks continue to degrade over time, emissions have to be lowered on a continuous basis well into the future. Total global emissions must not exceed the capacity of the global commons to absorb them, and that is likely to be less than half a gigaton per year.

The higher the chosen stabilisation level, the more difficult these feedbacks make it to maintain that level.

One fifth of global CO_2 emissions currently come from deforestation, a process which also destroys the capacity of the carbon sink. Ending deforestation is therefore a "double win", preventing emissions and preserving sinks.

Because of time-lags in the system, the path of climate change to 2030 is already set. Emissions cuts have to be made long before the need for them becomes apparent from observation.

Presentation 3: Anthropogenic Degrade of the Carbon Sinks

The destruction of rainforest ecosystems is continuing apace with virtually no restraining influence from the Kyoto Protocol. This presentation concentrates on Amazonia where deforestation now releases as much CO_2 into the atmosphere as the rest of the forest absorbs. Human activity has cancelled out the carbon sink of the Amazon rainforest.

The Amazon like all ecosystems is at risk of 'ecosystem failure', the end to the services like carbon sequestration and rain cloud production as a result of degradation by rising atmospheric radiative forcing. Global Climate Models suggest that for many of the earth's ecosystems this may be just a few decades away. Anthropogenic destruction of carbon sinks however, is a different and much more imminent threat. This is the active clearance of forest with the risk that a point may be reached where the remainder is no longer viable as a self-sustaining ecosystem and collapse would result. Critical early indicators of this include drought and frequent fire outbreak.

The drivers of deforestation stem from the financial rewards from industrial logging and monoculture expansion. These in turn are a response to the demand for timber, wood products, animal feed and vegetable oils. More recently there has been an acceleration in deforestation driven by the huge rise in demand from the bio-fuels industry. There is a direct relationship between the rate of Amazonian deforestation and the market price of soya.

Burn-back as part of the deforestation process releases carbon into the atmosphere from the ancient forest store. The pall of smoke also interrupts the evapo-transpiration cycle. The whole process increases the vulnerability of the Amazon forest to climate change, adding an anthropogenic feedback to the carbon cycle. Decrease in the ability of the system to recover from drought (lowered resilience) accelerates the natural climate-driven die back of the Amazon forest, so accelerating and intensifying the carbon feedbacks described in Presentation 2.

Major interruption in the extent of the canopy also destroys the sequential westward progression of rainfall and transpiration, setting off a cascade collapse of the ecosystem across the continent. This would lead to severe changes in global rainfall patterns, with substantial reductions over much of South America and as far North as the US mid-west.

The key factor is dehydration. Under drought conditions fires burn out of control. If much of the forest is dry or damaged, fires could grow into mega-fires. Under these conditions vast tracts may vanish permanently, raising the possibility that ecosystem destruction could lead to collapse on a very narrow time scale.

Some 500 gigatons of carbon are stored in the tropical rainforests of the world. 60% of that resides in the Amazon basin. Eco-system collapse here could therefore discharge many times the annual anthropogenic emission of CO_2. The process could take several decades to unfold, but once started it would be virtually unstoppable. It would put any future prospects of climate stabilisation completely beyond our control.

If we were able to make dramatic reductions in emissions from the burning of fossil fuels but failed to prevent further deforestation, we would still cross the point where climate feedbacks would make all our efforts irrelevant. We are now more likely to trigger runaway climate feedbacks as a result of ecosystem failure than we are as a result of profligate emissions from the use of fossil fuels.

Effective systemic solutions are now both urgent and imperative.

Presentation 4: Feedbacks in Ice and Ocean Dynamics

Antarctic ice cores show that we have gone through a number of glacial cycles in the past half million years. Each cycle also involves change in the level of atmospheric carbon dioxide from about 200 ppm during the glacial phase, to 300 ppm in the warm inter-glacials. In recent years, human activity has precipitated unprecedented and accelerating levels of CO_2 concentration. Average global temperature has followed suit.

14

If you add in the effects of other anthropogenic greenhouse gasses, coded in terms of CO_2-equivalence, then we already have a concentration of 440 ppm CO_{2e}, and the level is accelerating upwards. There is a general consensus that to avoid disastrously rapid warming we should stop at 450 ppm CO_{2e}. It is hard to see how that can be achieved when emissions are now double the rate of natural absorption.

In this context we are seeing the accelerated reduction of Arctic sea ice. It is shrinking in area and thinning dramatically. Average thickness has reduced by half in the last 25 years. The thickest areas of ridged ice have lost more than ¾ of their depth in the same period. Complete loss of Arctic sea ice in late summer is now expected during the 2030's, way in advance of any model predictions.

The process is driven by climate feedback, and also drives climate feedbacks. The change from ice cover to open water increases the rate of evaporation of water-vapour into the atmosphere. It also reduces the albedo effect, since much less energy is reflected back into space from open water than from ice. Both of these effects accelerate global warming.

As the climate warms, land-based snow cover decreases in extent and duration, so reducing albedo even further and adding to the feedback process.

The absence of sea ice from around the coasts of previously ice-bound land accelerates the rate of melt of land-based ice. This has a particularly marked effect on the Greenland ice-sheet, with implications for acceleration in the rise of sea-level. Increase in global warming also leads to higher temperatures in the ocean surface layer, increased expansion of ocean water volume and further acceleration in the rise of sea level.

Warming of the Arctic Ocean, increased precipitation and decrease in the formation of winter sea-ice are reducing the drivers of the "thermohaline circulation" and slowing the Gulf Stream. This will result in slower rise in temperature for north-western Europe, but hotter ocean temperatures further south. Southern Europe can expect a temperature rise of up to 4°C and more than 30% decrease in rainfall by the end of this century, as North African desert conditions extend across the Mediterranean.

Another ocean feedback is driven by increased acidification of the surface water. Acid water absorbs less CO_2. It also interferes with the ability of some plankton to form chalky shells, one of the long term processes by which CO_2 is removed from the atmosphere and sequestered on the ocean floor. Both of these feedbacks reduce the effectiveness of carbon sinks on which we depend for the absorption of anthropogenic emissions.

In conclusion, anthropogenic emissions of greenhouse gasses produce feedbacks that all tend to be positive (amplifying the rate of climate change). There is therefore a strong argument to achieve much more stringent reductions in carbon emissions than hitherto contemplated.

Presentation 5: Accelerated Climate Change and the Task of Stabilisation

Almost all of the systems known to affect climate change are now in a state of net positive (amplifying) feedback. Each feedback mechanism accelerates its own specific process. The output of each feedback is an input to all other feedbacks, so the system as a whole constitutes an interactive set of mutually reinforcing sub-systems. This "second order" feedback system accelerates the rate of climate change and faces us with the possibility of a "tipping point" in the whole earth system. If we go beyond the point where human intervention can no longer stabilise the system, then we precipitate unstoppable runaway climate change. That would set in motion a major extinction event comparable to the five other extinction crises that the earth has previously experienced.

A state of unstable equilibrium occurs in the natural system when amplifying positive feedback just balances the effects of naturally occurring negative (damping) feedback. Beyond that point positive feedback dominates and runaway change commences. The system can still be stabilised, but only while the power of human intervention is greater than the steadily increasing power of positive feedback.

There is a "critical threshold" in the system beyond which the power of positive feedback overwhelms the capacity for human intervention. The cost of intervention escalates towards infinity as that threshold is approached. The Stern Report noted that the sooner we intervene, the lower would be the cost of climate stabilisation. It did not take into account the existence of a critical threshold beyond which effective intervention becomes impossible. This new analysis turns the accepted economics of mitigation on its head. The situation is represented in the diagram overleaf.

That is a huge strategic shift in our understanding of climate change. It has not been taken into account in the Kyoto negotiations. It has not been taken into account in current European legislation. It has not been taken into account in the framing of the Climate Bill brought before the UK Parliament.

We are now in the early stages of runaway climate change. There does not appear to be any naturally occurring negative feedback process available to contain its effects. Strategically we have to generate a negative feedback intervention of sufficient power to overcome the now active positive feedback process. We then have to maintain its effectiveness during the remaining period

16

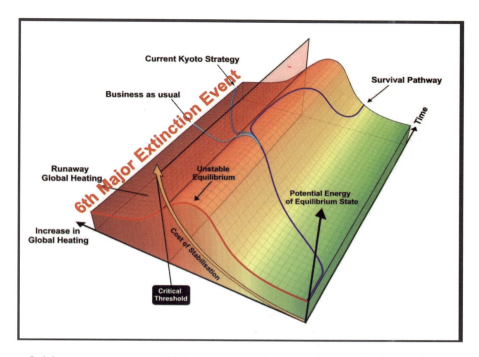

of rising temperature, while temperature-driven positive feedbacks continue to operate. That is an extraordinarily difficult task, out of all comparison with strategies currently in place.

The presentation concludes with a study of the dynamics of radiative forcing in order to illustrate the strategic intervention now required.

David Wasdell
Director of the Apollo-Gaia Project
Madrid
23rd September 2007

17

Presentation One:

An Introduction to Climate Dynamics

David Wasdell

This opening presentation provides a general introduction to climate dynamics and to the system of feedback mechanisms within it.

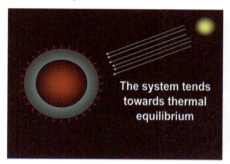

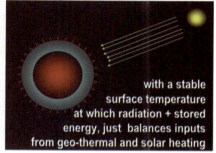

| *Figure 1.1* | *Figure 1.2* |

We begin by viewing the earth hanging in space as a "hot black body" giving out infra-red radiation through its mantle of the atmosphere, and receiving energy from solar input.

It achieves a stable surface temperature with radiation just balancing inputs of energy from outside the system. That is what we would call climate in an equilibrium state. To be sure, over the last one million years, temperatures have varied from ice-ages to warm inter-glacial periods, but the climate has stayed roughly in equilibrium during those transitions.

Until homo sapiens arrived on the scene and decided that instead of just working with what we could harvest from solar inputs year by year, we would dig up the remnants of solar energy from millions of years ago and use that as well.

In so doing we set off a population explosion which reached about 2.3 billion by the middle of the twentieth century, and now stands at 6.5 billion. It is likely to peak at between 9.5 and 10 billion by 2050, though any such prediction is subject to a wide range of contingencies.

Population growth throughout history

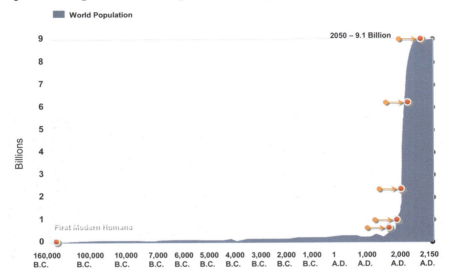

Figure 1.3

Figure 1.4

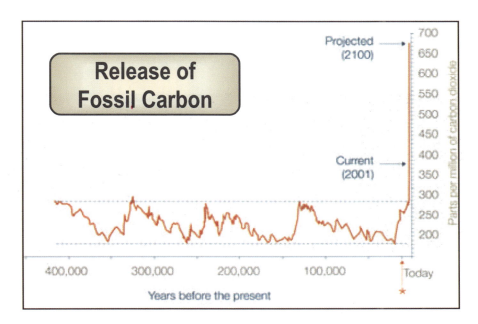

Figure 1.5

As one of the inadvertent polluting by-products, we released back into the atmosphere the carbon that had been biologically sequestrated to cool the earth in the natural process of things over many millions of years. This has pushed the concentration of atmospheric carbon dioxide way outside the pattern of variation over the last 400,000, to 1 million years.

Figure 1.6

Figure 1.7

It currently stands at around 384 parts per million (ppm), and it is projected (under the "business as usual" scenario) to go up towards the 650 ppm by the year 2100.

Increasing the concentration of greenhouse gasses raises the efficiency of the "duvet", the insulating atmospheric mantle. It reduces the outgoing radiation. That in turn begins to drive up the temperature of the surface.

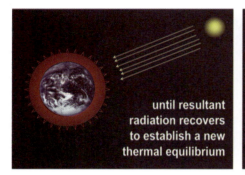

until resultant radiation recovers to establish a new thermal equilibrium

Except that we are accelerating the accumulation of GHGs, and feedbacks are also pushing the system even further from balance

Figure 1.8   *Figure 1.9*

The temperature goes on going up until thermal equilibrium is re-established, at which outgoing radiation from a hotter surface just balances input of energy from the sun. Or at least that is the theory.

In practice the increase in concentration of greenhouse gasses is not a single "step" change. It is a continuous and accelerating process. We are continuously improving the tog of the duvet, so it gets hotter and hotter in bed, and cooler in the room outside. The temperature goes on increasing, accelerated by the effects of positive feedback. The time-lag between the current surface temperature and the attainment of eventual equilibrium becomes bigger and bigger.

At this point we move on from the initial presentation of the thermodynamics of the whole earth in its spatial context. In the next section, we begin to explore the set of factors that drive climate change and the system of positive feedback mechanisms that threaten to push it into uncontrollable behaviour.

A conceptual model of feedback dynamics

The system that governs the behaviour of the climate is made up of many elements and they are also subject to feedbacks which accelerate their effect on the problem. We will now develop a conceptual model of feedback dynamics and start with the very basic drivers of the climate system.

Geo-thermal energy is pretty stable. It is comparatively small, and changes over very long time-scales, so for our purposes we are going to ignore it. Solar energy obviously is the main heater. The elements that drive change in global heating are represented by the green boxes in the lower part of the slide.

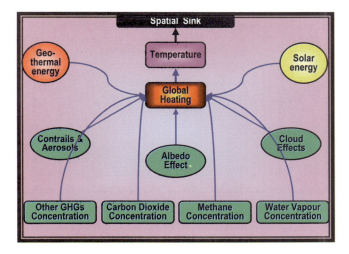

Figure 1.10

Increase in carbon dioxide concentration drives the greenhouse effect, as does methane release. Other greenhouse gasses, the nitrous oxides, the CFCs, and ozone also contribute to global heating. Contrails and aerosols, aircraft trails and particles in the atmosphere, also make a difference, as do water vapour concentration and cloud effects. Albedo, the reflection of solar radiation from land surface, vegetation, oceans and ice, completes the set of elements in the overall climate system. They drive global heating – technically radiative forcing – and slowly that pushes the temperature up, and that eventually enables more energy to radiate out to the spatial sink.

Now we can introduce the feedback system. (See Figure 1.11) We have identified 8 categories of feedback here and there is still one in hiding which I will introduce in a moment. Feedback categories may each contain many feedback mechanisms and I am going to give you a brief introduction to that system before handing on to Peter Cox to look in detail at what is going on in the carbon cycle.

The feedback Category **F1**, is driven by rising carbon dioxide concentration. It effects and accelerates change in carbon dioxide concentration. It also has some minor effects on the albedo. All other categories are driven by rising temperature. The hotter it gets, the faster it gets hotter!

23

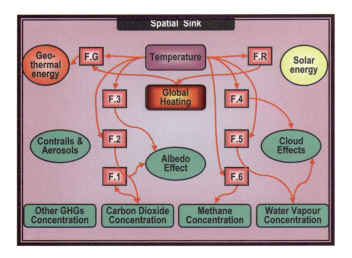

Figure 1.11

F2 is temperature driven and affects carbon dioxide concentration. **F3**, also temperature driven, changes the albedo effect. **F4**, temperature-driven, works on clouds. **F5**, changes water-vapour concentration, and finally, **F6** is temperature driven and works on the methane cycle. The feedback category relating to solar radiation is also important, and I will speak about that in a moment.

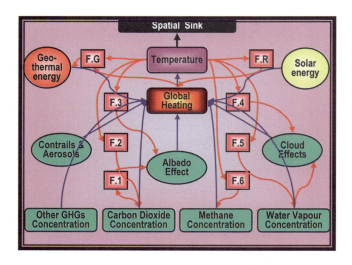

Figure 1.12

24

Now we can combine feedbacks and the standard drivers. And this slide has many active links. If I click on "Solar Energy", it opens up the radiation cycle.

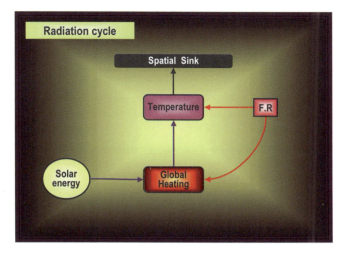

Figure 1.13

Solar energy, trapped by the greenhouse effect, drives global heating. Slowly (because the thermal inertia of the earth is so massive) temperature goes up. More energy is eventually radiated back out to the spatial sink.

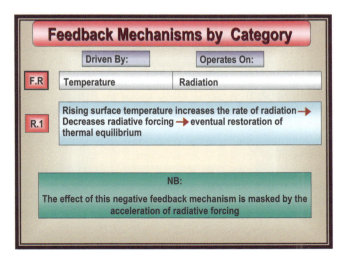

Figure 1.14

25

There is a feedback category in this cycle that we can explore. It is driven by rising temperature and effects the rate of radiation.

Rising temperature of the surface of the earth increases the rate of radiation into space, so that discharges the tension between inputs and outputs and would eventually restore thermal equilibrium. Except of course that we are making it worse all the time, so the effect of that feedback mechanism is masked by our acceleration of radiative forcing.

Next we can explore the carbon cycle. I will give a brief summary before the detail is covered by Peter Cox.

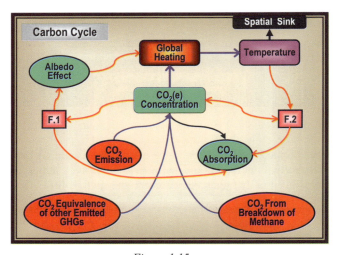

Figure 1.15

CO_2 emissions from all sources, other greenhouse gasses put here as CO_2 equivalents, and CO_2 from the breakdown of methane in the atmosphere – all contribute to the CO_2 equivalent concentration. There is a sink that absorbs some of that back into the land and the ocean and the vegetation. The rest of it contributes to radiative forcing – global heating.

Let us now turn to the feedback categories in the carbon cycle, **F1**, **F2**. For instance, in Feedback **1.1**, rising CO_2 concentration leads to acidification of the ocean water and highly acidic water does not take up so much CO_2, so that is a positive (amplifying) feedback. No.**1.2** – plankton do not thrive in acid water, so we get an increasing destruction of plankton and therefore the sink that they represent also starts to degrade.

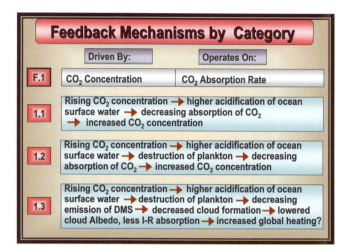

Figure 1.16

1.3 is a technical one. As the plankton population goes down they give out less dimethyl sulphide. It is a gas which breaks down in the atmosphere to create tiny crystals of sulphur around which droplets of water form. As a consequence the cloud does not form as well over the derelict seas that have become too hot for plankton to operate. That feedback is an ambiguous one, with lowered albedo compensated by lowered absorption of infra-red radiation.

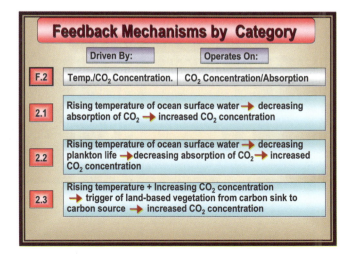

Figure 1.17

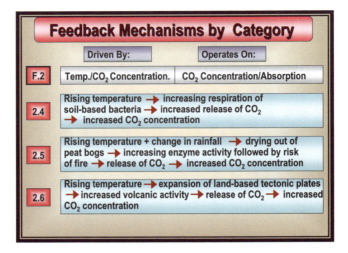

Figure 1.18

Figures 1.17 and *1.18* outline six feedback mechanisms in the carbon cycle that are driven by rising temperature, and Peter Cox will address these in detail.

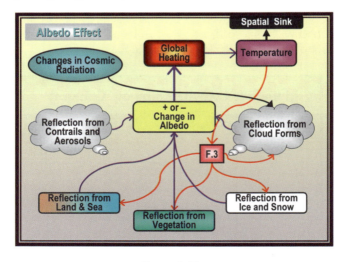

Figure 1.19

Next we take a look at the albedo cycle. Reflections from all surfaces, land and sea, vegetation, and ice and snow, change the albedo effect positively or negatively, so changing the reflection of energy back out into space.

There is reflection from aircraft trails and aerosols in the atmosphere and from natural cloud formations. There is also a small input from changes in cosmic radiation, which over a 22 year cycle of sunspot activity, changes the way clouds form. We can ignore that unless it happens at a very sensitive point in the system's behaviour.

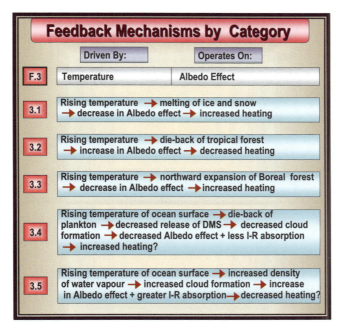

Figure 1.20

Figure 1.20 outlines the various feedback mechanisms in the category **F3**. Some of this will be Peter Wadham's domain. Temperatures go up, melting ice and snow, less reflection, more absorption, increased heating. Dieback of tropical forest, increased albedo effect – because savannah reflects more than forest does – decreased heating, that is a negative feedback. (But by the way, as Deepak Rughani will be noting, a massive amount of carbon is released into the atmosphere as the forests die back. The vegetation also ceases to act as a carbon sink, which is something that Peter Cox will be looking at.) Rising temperatures lead to northward expansion of the northern forests. The tundra reflects a lot of light, particularly with snow on it, but forests do not. So we get a decreased albedo and that is a positive feedback. Then there is the die back of plankton with reduction of cloud albedo, but increase of cloud albedo because higher temperatures lead to more water vapour and more clouds.

29

We will look briefly at two more cycles. First, the methane cycle, with methane generated by human, plant, animal, and bacterial activity.

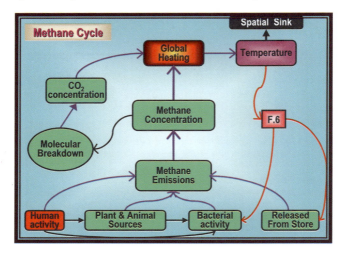

Figure 1.21

Of course human activity not only leads to methane emission in its own right, but also affects the outputs from animals, plants and bacteria. The methane output from the cows in India is significant. Somebody is trying to work on genetic modification to prevent cows emitting so much methane. Bacteria have outputs in their own right, but bacterial activity in landfill sites also creates methane some of which discharges into the atmosphere.

Then there is methane stored in frozen conditions in the tundra and also in the clathrates – the concentrations of methane in the rotted vegetation held frozen in crystalline form on the ocean floor by a combination of temperature and pressure. So that completes the set of methane emissions which drives up the concentration. Chemically, methane does break down in the atmosphere eventually into water vapour and CO_2, so that inputs to the carbon cycle. As a greenhouse gas methane is some 23 times more powerful than Carbon dioxide. It drives global heating and contributes to the rising temperature.

Feedbacks in this zone are temperature driven: So, the hotter the temperature, the more bacterial activity, more methane is emitted. Thawing of tundra permafrost releases methane, increases greenhouse gas and increases global heating. Finally, the well known one, the warming of the shallow seas could start to release the methane held in frozen crystal form in the sea bed and that would be a long term but potentially very powerful dynamic feedback.

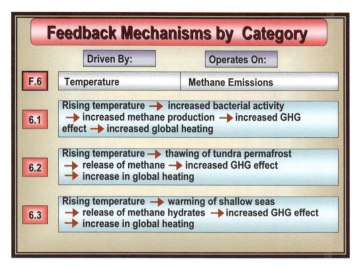

Figure 1.22

The final cycle concerns water vapour.

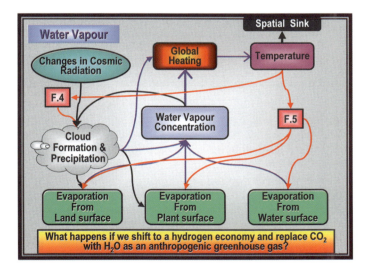

Figure 1.23

Evaporation from all surfaces increases the concentration of water vapour, some of it then condenses to form clouds and rains back to earth. I didn't bother to put rain onto the sea because it is as wet as it is, whether it has rain falling on it or not, and it does not change the evaporation rate!

F4 changes what is going on in the clouds, it is pretty small as a feedback source and I am ignoring it today.

The feedback category **F5** is temperature driven and affects what is happening in the water vapour cycle. Meanwhile small changes in cosmic radiation affect cloud formation. Lastly, the question is often raised: "What happens if we all go to a hydrogen economy? Doesn't that put out water vapour? Isn't that a green house gas? Wouldn't that change the situation?" The answer to that is that the amount of CO_2 we have put out is significant compared to what is up there already. If we put out water vapour the amount is absolutely minuscule compared to the amount of water vapour already in the atmosphere. Forget it, we can safely have a hydrogen economy.

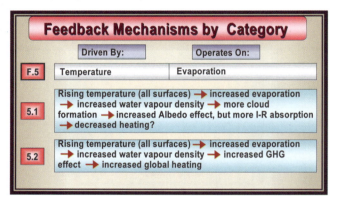

Figure 1.24

Feedback **5.1**, rising temperature, increased evaporation, increased water vapour density and its effect on clouds, is an ambiguous mechanism: – more clouds, more reflection of sunlight, but more blocking of infrared heating and radiation. So not quite sure how that one goes.

5.2: Rising temperature at all surfaces leads to increased evaporation, increased water vapour density, increased green house gas effect from the (uncondensed) water vapour. Water vapour constitutes the most profoundly dominant greenhouse gas. There are massive amounts in the atmosphere. What we are looking at are the slight changes in that amount caused by rising temperature. This fast-acting feedback mechanism becomes more and more significant as the temperature starts to rise.

In the final section I want to pay attention to the **"Thermal Inertia"** of the earth. There is a long time lag between the heat engine turning up the power and temperature following suit. Thermal inertia of the earth is massive.

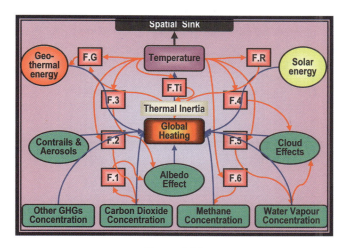

Figure 1.25

There is another feedback category (**F.Ti**) that is driven by rising temperature and changes the thermal inertia, so altering the rate at which temperature rises. That in turn affects the behaviour of all the other temperature-driven feedback mechanisms. Radiative forcing, drives up the rate of heating, leading eventually to change in temperature. In *Figure 1.26*, I am going to explore all the various mechanisms that take up the heat energy and moderate the change in global temperature. Global heating slowly warms the ocean surface. That takes a lot of energy, and the mixing takes the heat down into the deeper water. Heating of ice. That is by conduction and takes up much less energy.

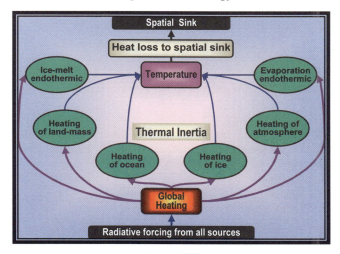

Figure 1.26

Heating of land mass is quite quick as also is the warming of the atmosphere. Melting of ice takes up energy. You have to input energy to melt ice in water. So that keeps temperatures down while the energy is being taken up in the volume of melted ice. Finally we have the evaporation of water – change of phase from liquid to gas also absorbs energy. It is "endothermic". So there is a cooling effect there. The temperature rise is damped by these last two endothermic mechanisms.

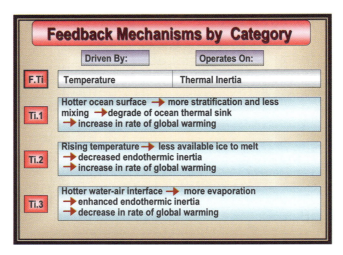

Figure 1.27

There is a feedback loop between the rising temperature and thermal inertia.

In **Ti.1**, the hotter the surface water of the sea becomes, the more stratification occurs in the upper layers of the ocean. Warmer water is less dense and stays at the top. There is less mixing, and that decreases the efficiency of the oceanic thermal sink. That is a positive feedback that increases the rate of global warming.

Secondly, in **Ti.2**, as the ice melts there is less volume of ice available to melt. At the higher latitudes the area of ice shrinks as the ice retracts. Similarly, as you go up mountains the areas of snow and ice shrink the higher you go. So the thermal inertia due to ice-melt decreases with rising temperature (another positive feedback that increases the rate of temperature increase). However, this feedback decreases in power as areas become ice-free.

And finally a damper (or negative feedback). The hotter the water/air interface, the more evaporation, and so more cooling. The more sea levels rise and the less the area of sea-ice, the greater the area of water available for evaporation. That slightly slows the rate of temperature increase.

So that completes the set of feedback categories with their various mechanisms and effects that, taken all together, drive climate dynamics.

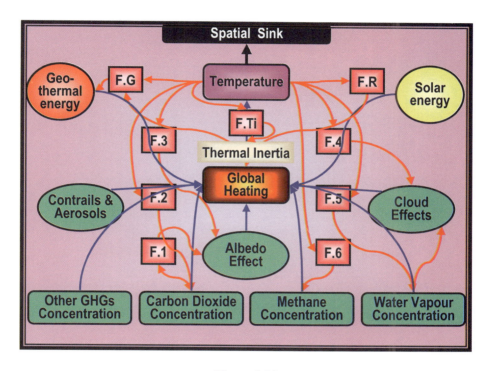

Figure 1.28

Presentation Two:
Feedback Dynamics of the Carbon Cycle

Peter Cox

I am going to talk specifically about interactions between physical climate change and uptake of carbon dioxide by the ocean and land, and this is one of the feedbacks that David mentioned. I think it is an especially important one because it highlights not just the fact that climate change with a given amount of emissions could be faster than we thought, it also has a direct impact on how hard we have to work to stabilise CO_2 in the atmosphere. This is why I called it 'Changing Perspectives of the Climate Problem'.

I think in many ways climate modellers like myself are being asked a new set of questions now, which is no longer 'what happens if we do nothing?', rather 'what do we have to do to avoid dangerous change?' And what I am going to talk about, has an impact on what we might define as dangerous change and also how hard we have to work to avoid it.

The main thing to note, and this is often forgotten, is that the natural carbon cycle, that is the vegetation and the soil on the land, and the ocean, have been performing a really excellent service for us to date by absorbing about half of our emissions, roughly speaking. So when we look at how fast the carbon dioxide goes up in the atmosphere, and it is quite fast, it is about 0.5% per year, it is about half of what you would expect given our emissions, so these natural systems are, in a sense, buffering us from some of the effects of climate change.

We have become a bit blasé about this and have made assumptions that really boil down to believing that would continue to be the case, and what I am going to tell you is, try to indicate to you at least, is that climate change may well suppress the ability of these things to operate in our favour. *Figure 2.1* shows the carbon balance as estimated by the last IPCC Report. So in terms of fossil fuel emissions and cement, 7.2 billion tons in the form of CO_2 goes out per year and the atmospheric increase is only 4.1, which is 57% of that. The rest is being taken up by the ocean. CO_2 dissolves in the ocean, it is used by phytoplankton to form shells and so on, and there is a pump of CO_2 to ocean depth, which takes it out of the atmosphere. Photosynthesis absorbs CO_2 as well, and the carbon that is absorbed is stored in the vegetation itself and mainly in the soils.

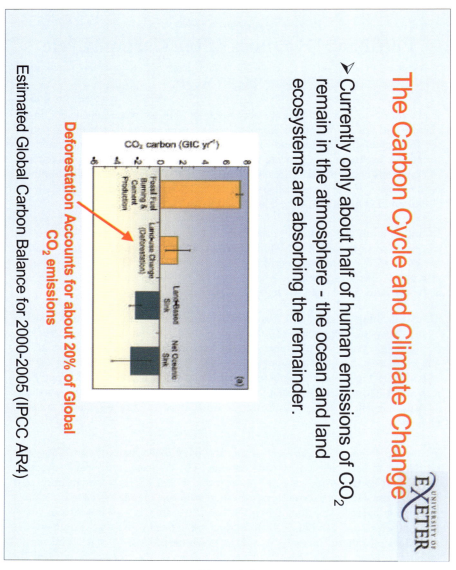

Figure 2.1

So at the moment we have got about 50%, and this varies from year to year, but roughly speaking, 50% of our CO_2 emissions are being removed. This is just the bar chart showing that. So on the left here we have got the fossil fuel emissions of about 7, and I want to draw your attention to the second bar - Deepak will talk a bit more about this, at least 20% of the global CO_2 emissions actually come from deforestation, they are not from fossil fuel burning. There are lots of reasons why we would want to avoid deforestation and I think that is something we will probably come back to in discussion, but remember deforestation accounts for about 20% of global CO_2 emissions. We are necessarily interested in the fossil fuel part because that has been growing fastest, but avoiding deforestation has other positive impacts that we will hear about. The main thing is that the "natural" carbon cycle has been acting in our favour, absorbing about half of our emissions and slowing down climate change.

But we also know that the processes responsible for those absorptions are sensitive to climate.

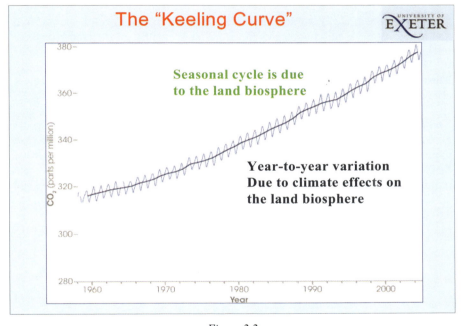

Figure 2.2

I am going to show you the Keeling Curve here which is the CO_2 record from Hawaii, which really highlighted the whole issue of increasing CO_2 in the atmosphere. You can see this goes from in the late '50s from about 320 ppm and is now up above 380 ppm. You will see a wiggle and that is associated with the fact that vegetation grows during the summer time in the northern hemisphere and takes CO_2 out of the atmosphere and there is a net release during the winter time. Because we have got more land in the northern hemisphere than the southern hemisphere there is a net cycle, with CO_2 drawn down during the

39

summer in the northern hemisphere and released during the northern hemisphere winter. The other thing to note, if you look at the continuous line, that is the year on year average value and you can see that that goes up all the time because of increasing emissions, but it also has flat spots and these are associated with the response of the land in particular to climate variations, natural climate variations in many cases. So for example in the early '90s there is a flat spot there you can just about make out. That was when Mount Pinatubo exploded and it cooled the climate system down by throwing aerosol particles up into the atmosphere and slowed down the CO_2 increase. So we have empirical evidence that the natural carbon cycle responds to climate variations and there is really no reason to believe that it would not also respond to climate change driven by us and that has been the concern.

So the seasonal cycle is due to the land biosphere's response to the seasons and the year to year variation is due to climate effects, mainly on the land biosphere but also on the ocean uptake through wind speeds and so on.

Most climate models prescribe atmospheric CO2 and therefore neglect climate-carbon cycle feedbacks.

And until the IPCC report before last, and this is still generally the case, most climate modellers prescribed the increase in atmospheric carbon dioxide and therefore neglected these feedbacks. What I want to talk to you about now is what their implications are for the rate of climate change and the emissions cuts required to achieve stabilisation of CO_2.

The question we are asking is 'how will these neglected carbon cycle feedbacks affect future climate change?'

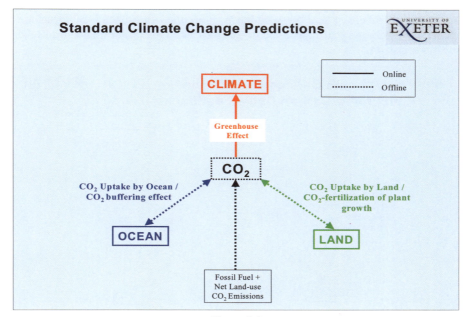

Figure 2.3

Here is a slightly different variant of the sort of feedback charts that David showed. This is the way we do standard climate projections typically, so the dotted lines mean that this is outside of the climate model, it is essentially a driving external factor. So we take a climate model represented by the red box and we drive it with increases in greenhouse gasses, especially CO_2 but not solely, which is calculated off-line, that means without reference to the climate change itself, and takes account of the fact that oceans absorb CO_2 by being dissolved in sea water. The land vegetation tends to respond if everything else is OK by growing more strongly if CO_2 is high, assuming you have got lots of nitrogen in the water. So the standard way of doing climate projections basically says CO_2 has an impact on the uptake by these natural sinks but climate doesn't.

What we are asking is, if you take a more realistic view like that shown here (in *Figure 2.4*,) now when the climate changes, that clearly has an impact on things like where vegetation can grow, how strongly it can grow, certainly if the water availability changes, if the rainfall patterns change we expect the pattern of vegetation across the globe and the productivity of vegetation to change.

On the left hand side you can also see there are effects, David mentioned one of these, the solubility of CO_2 goes down as the ocean surface warms. As you warm the ocean surface there is less mixing to depth, which means less of the CO_2 ends up at depth where it can be withdrawn from the atmosphere, so these are generally feedbacks that reduce the extent to which these natural sinks can take up our emissions.

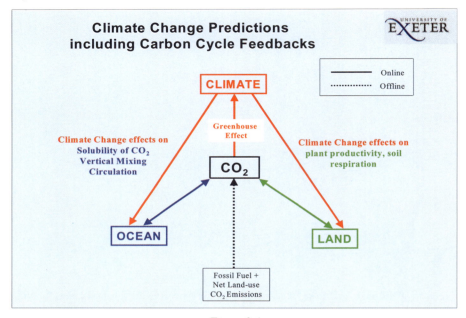

Figure 2.4

When we tried to assess this in the Hadley Centre's model we found results that are represented here.

Figure 2.5 looks a bit complex but if you look at the top right first, this is the bottom line really, even though it is the top right. The blue line there is the sort of scenario David was talking about. This is what used to be known as the 'business as usual scenario'. This is about central in terms of what is possible for emissions over the next hundred years and it leads to a CO_2 by the end of the century of about 700 ppm from the 280 ppm that we started at in say, 1750. If you look at the red line then you can see what happens if we add these additional feedbacks. So for a given amount of emissions we don't get 750 ppm but we get nearly 1000 ppm, so a big acceleration in the CO_2 in the atmosphere, and because CO_2 is a greenhouse gas, a greater rate of warming.

And at the bottom you can see why that happens. So the blue line again is in the absence of climate feedbacks and the land takes up roughly speaking about 5 billion tons of carbon per year by the end of the century, if you neglect these feedbacks. The red line shows what happens if you don't. Then the land does

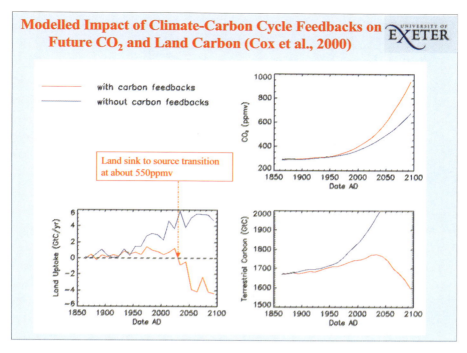

Figure 2.5

not take up anywhere near as much, and in fact it stops taking up CO_2 altogether in this particular model, and starts to emit it. So instead of doing what it has been doing which is slowing down climate change, in this model the land starts to exacerbate the problem. And in some senses you would say that is the definition of a dangerous change because that is the point at which the system starts to accelerate or exacerbate the problem that we are causing.

And in this model (Figure 2.6, over) this Hadley Centre model, there is also a very dramatic reduction of the forest cover in Amazonia which is associated with drying in that region, so an impact on the carbon cycle but also on biodiversity and all of the things that are required to support people and animals there.

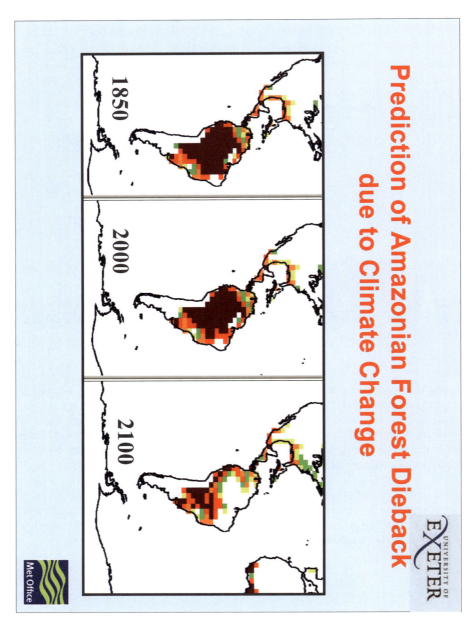

Figure 2.6

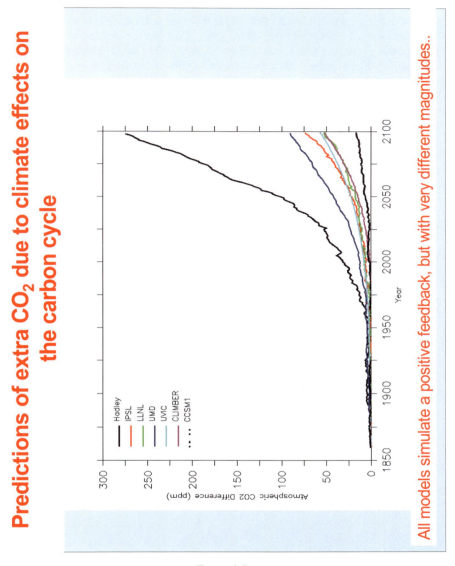

Figure 2.7

However, and this is a common thing that we will see all the time in climate predictions, there is great uncertainty and there is always a danger that the uncertainty is something that justifies us not acting. The opposite is the case. And this is just to show you what the uncertainty is. Here is a set of seven models that have now done similar experiments and what we have got plotted here is the extra carbon dioxide that arises from these feedbacks over and above what was normally assumed from the models. You can see that the model I have been showing you, the black one at the top, has a very large positive feedback, more than 200 ppm more CO_2 just from the feedback by the end of the century. But other models are lower and the average is more like 80 ppm, which is very significant, it is a very significant amplification, but that means we have to live with this uncertainty and we have to find ways to deal with an uncertain future and not let it cripple policy.

So what do we need to do to stabilise the atmospheric CO_2 concentration? What I have been showing you to date really is what happens to the climate system if we just put out a certain amount of emissions per year and grow it in some way that we prescribe. The real issue is 'how much do we have to cut emissions to stabilise CO_2 at a level that avoids dangerous change?' and that is also impacted by how effective these sinks are at absorbing our emissions.

Below is a profile produced by my colleague at Hadley Centre, Chris Jones, and myself for a recent paper. These are scenarios of global CO_2 emissions and how they vary through time up to 2300, so a long way ahead for two stabilisation levels, one at 550 ppm and one at 450 ppm. The red is with the carbon cycle feedback and the blue is without, so the blue is what we used to assume and the

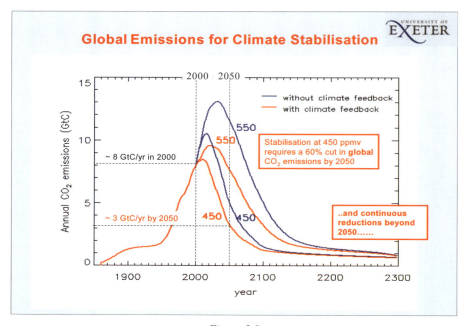

Figure 2.8

46

red is what we think, we fear, may be the case if we treat the system in a more integrated and coupled way.

So if you look for example at the 450 ppm you have to start reducing emissions much quicker if this feedback is as accelerating as we think it might be. If you look at the red 450 ppm line then you have to go from about the 8 billion tons per year that we are putting out now to approximately 3 billion tons by 2050 which turns out to be a 60% cut in **global** CO_2 emissions. I highlight "**global**" because this means of course that, if we are going to go for contraction and convergence, it means a much bigger cut in terms of the developed world in terms of the amount of cut you have to do, but that is the figure for the global. The other thing to note about this is that that is not the end of it, it is just the beginning, because you have to keep reducing the CO_2 emissions from that level until you get to the background sinks, which are a few tenths, or maybe half a gigaton of carbon per year. It is a long tail in other words. The hardest bit is to get over the hump, but once you are there you have to keep pushing it down. So we require continuous reductions beyond 2050. That is now always recognised, that you have to continue to reduce the emissions.

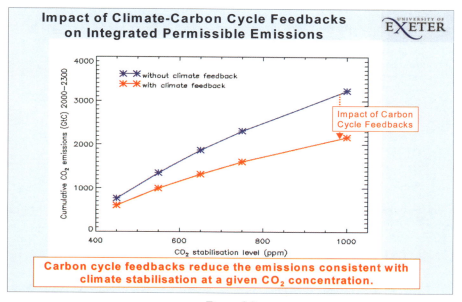

Figure 2.9

This is just showing you, if you change your stabilisation level along the bottom, what the impact of these carbon cycle feedbacks would be on the total amount of emissions you are allowed to put out between now and the end of the 24th century, most of which would be in the next 100 years. And this is really to show you that the impact of the carbon cycle feedback becomes more and more detrimental in terms of the rate which you have to cut as you go to higher levels of stabilisation. There is still an argument about where we should be on this x-axis, but the carbon cycle feedback says back towards the lower levels if anything because it gets harder to stabilise as you go further out.

This next slide (See *Figure 2.10*) is taking a bit of a liberty here because of where I am in the presentation sequence. Deepak is going to talk about this. One of the things we have to do of course is to find easy ways to start and things that have co-benefits that are useful and one of them is avoiding deforestation.

"Avoided Deforestation" :
:a win-win option ?

➢ **Tropical deforestation accounts for about 20% of global CO_2 emissions (cf. the 5% cut aimed for by the Kyoto Protocol).**

➢ **An area of Amazonian forest the size of Belgium is cleared each year accounting for about 7% of global CO_2 emissions alone, and ultimately putting 5-10% of the Earth's species at risk.**

➢ **The Kyoto Protocol of the United Nations Framework Convention on Climate Change allows the signatories of the protocol to partially offset their national emissions with CO_2 uptake by "managed forests".**

➢ **However, "avoided deforestation" is deliberately excluded from the Kyoto Protocol.**

➢ **Including mechanisms to reward avoided deforestation should be a priority for the follow-on to the Kyoto Protocol.**

Figure 2.10

As I said before in that first plot, 20% of global CO_2 emissions actually come from deforestation, mainly in the tropics. An area of the Amazonian forest the size of Belgium is cleared each year, accounting for about 7% of global CO_2 emissions and putting a lot of biodiversity at risk of course. Unfortunately we don't really have joined up policy because the Kyoto Protocol does not actually easily provide incentives for avoiding deforestation and I am glad to hear that there is a move towards including avoiding deforestation in the follow on to Kyoto which would be a win/win in my opinion.

OK I am just going to conclude. The earth's climate is warming and this is largely due to greenhouse gas increases, especially CO_2 - this is as clear as day. As David said, the climate system has a long memory and this means 2 things: first of all it means that further climate change out to 2030 is inevitable. We know what we are going to have to adapt to and it is almost independent of CO_2 emissions from now until then. Politically that is rather a difficult thing, because it means people are acting on behalf of future generations. But it also means that emission cuts, because of the lags in the system, must actually take place long before dangerous climate change would occur, so there is a need to have foresight of what is happening in the system. Climate change beyond this 2030 depends on CO_2 emissions which are in a sense humankind's choice, and earth systems feedbacks, one of which I have spoken to you about. Both are uncertain. We must not kid ourselves that if we wait long enough the uncertainty is going to reduce to a level where we say that is the answer, follow it. It won't be like that. There has to be some sort of adaptive policy or else we are going to get frozen by the uncertainty.

The main part of what I was talking about was the carbon cycle - Climate carbon cycle feedbacks - and they are likely to increase the CO_2 emission reductions required to stabilise at a given concentration of CO_2, so that means greater emission cuts than we might have previously thought. The strongest of these climate carbon cycle feedbacks that I showed you, for a stabilisation of CO_2 at 450 ppm, requires a 60% cut in global emissions by 2050 and more like 90% by 2100 because you have to continue pushing the thing down.

As I said tropical deforestation currently contributes about one-fifth of global CO_2 emissions and results in lots of things like loss of biodiversity, so in my opinion avoiding deforestation should be top priority for inclusion to the follow on to the Kyoto Protocol.

Conclusions & implications for policy

➤ The Earth's climate is warming and this is largely due to greenhouse gas increases (especially CO_2) associated with human-activities (especially fossil fuel burning and deforestation).

➤ The climate system has a "memory" which means :

    a) Further climate change to 2030 is inevitable, almost independently of CO_2 emissions.

    b) Emissions cuts must take place long before dangerous climate change would occur.

➤ Climate change beyond 2030 depends on CO_2 emissions and Earth system feedbacks, both of which are uncertain.

So policy must deal with significant uncertainty in the science but must not be frozen by it.

Figure 2.11

Presentation Three:
Anthropogenic Degrade of the Carbon Sinks

Deepak Rughani

Thank you Peter for cueing me to come in here. One of the missing ingredients is the risks we face around Ecosystems also described as Carbon Sinks, because they are repositories for carbon within the earth/climate system. Peter has already said that 50% of our emissions are absorbed, 25% by the oceans, 25% by the terrestrial system and it is this land-based store, particularly the rainforest ecosystems which I would like to consider right now.

It is pretty obvious that the drivers for climate change include fossil fuel burning. That's a primary factor and without the radiative forcing that fossil fuel emissions generate we would not be here talking about the accelerating feedbacks that could take us to a point of potentially catastrophic climate change, where it becomes unstoppable by human intervention. We could cross this point within a period of as little as a decade - Jim Hansen talks about needing to bring this whole thing under control within 10 years – but the unsaid aspect is that ecosystem destruction is continuing apace with virtually no restraining influence from the Kyoto Protocol, so we have to start looking at why it is absent and what the implications are of not addressing this.

So I have described deforestation as accelerating eco-system failure.

"Ecosystem Failure" is the point where ecosystems cease to perform their vital functions, i.e. they cease to provide the myriad services that they are ecologically fitted to provide. In particular two areas stand out associated with climate: the first is carbon absorption or sequestration capacity which forests provide – the Amazon for example draws about half a Gigaton of carbon each year. A Gigaton is a billion tons. We produce from fossil fuels about 7 gigatons annually, so we are talking about 1/14, quite a substantial uptake. Ridiculously by our deforestation we are actually adding about half a gigaton from the Amazon Basin alone, so we have null-return in terms of the absorptive capacity there.

The other aspect of ecosystem failure is the potential for a dramatic reduction in the capacity of the forest to absorb water and to transpire it out again thus contributing to the humid air mass that drives rainfall patterns in the Northern hemisphere.

Figure 3.1

So forests are of critical importance to us. Looking at the drivers of forest destruction – and we're talking about *old* growth forest destruction here – plantation forests aren't such a problem they hold comparatively little carbon, hence part of the irrelevance of off-setting. Industrial logging – clearly that is a big driver - also mono-culture crop expansion.

The two often go hand-in-hand and frequently involve the same companies. The underpinning elements here are the enormous commodity markets driving demand for timber, wood products, animal feed, vegetable oils for foods, for cosmetics, and a new contender over the last 2 to 3 years an absolutely huge increase in demand from the biofuels industry. Grown as vast monocultures principally through removing original ecosystems, what is described as land-use change.

Amazonia is really the focus of this presentation - 7 million square kilometres, so we are talking about a colossal area.

It looks fairly intact from this picture, (See *Figure 3.2*) but actually when you start to look closer it has a number of weak spots, breaks in the canopy stretching in some cases thousands of kilometres that potentially can accelerate climate change, ahead of the radiative forcings that we have just been talking about. And you can see this variation in terms of dehydration – the yellow areas - in different parts of the Amazon.

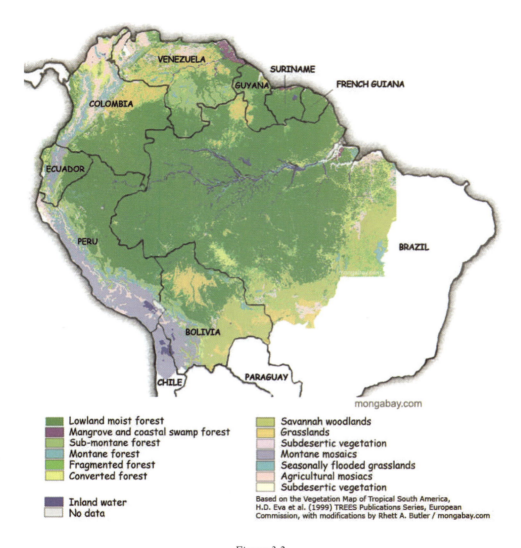

Lowland moist forest
Mangrove and coastal swamp forest
Sub-montane forest
Montane forest
Fragmented forest
Converted forest

Inland water
No data

Savannah woodlands
Grasslands
Subdesertic vegetation
Montane mosaics
Seasonally flooded grasslands
Agricultural mosiacs
Subdesertic vegetation

Based on the Vegetation Map of Tropical South America,
H.D. Eva et al. (1999) TREES Publications Series, European
Commission, with modifications by Rhett A. Butler / mongabay.com

Figure 3.2

The first wave of destruction that the Amazon has faced (and still faces) was from loggers, the second wave from cattle ranching, again still there, and the current one now is from soya production not just for food production which has a 10 – 15 year history but now massive additional pressure from biofuels production.

Amazon Deforestation

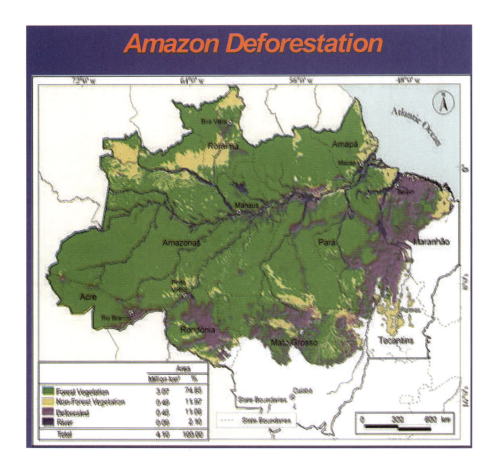

Figure 3.3

Many challenges with deforestation. The fires are one – smoke causes a cooling effect which dramatically reduces the evapo-transpiration process I talked about previously. But they also face the obvious challenge of fires getting out of control, particularly in the dry season. There have been lots of studies on this now. We seem to do very well in terms of studying the details of climate change whilst doing very little about it.

Figure 3.5 describes the link between deforestation for Soya and market forces globally. Research by NASA Earth Observatory have found a direct correlation between the price of soya on the international markets and the rate of deforestation in the Amazon.

Figure 3.4—forest clearance for soya plantations

This is a real cause for concern because it means that as we start opening the fuel market to Soya by virtue of biofuels on top of the food market, suddenly prices are going to rise alarmingly. And this is the situation we are currently facing. Deforestation for Soya becomes much more profitable and therefore harder to prevent as market prices escalate.

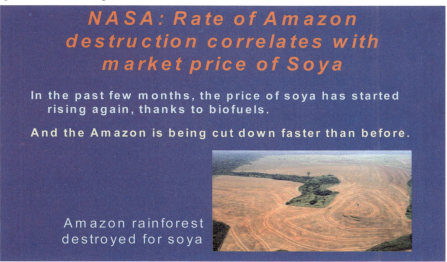

Figure 3.5

Figure 3.6—damaged forest is most susceptible to fire

This is an interesting picture because you can see from the foreground that the forest has actually been burnt once before and that might have happened fairly recently and makes the suggestion that burnt forest becomes much more vulnerable than humid moist forest that has remained intact.

Last year in late September satellite photography picked up 75,000 discrete fires in the Amazon at one go. At a certain point in time when it becomes too dry, clearly some of these fires may get out of control and merge together producing mega-fires and at that point we are very likely to see collapse of parts of the Amazon. It might not be wholesale that year but it will be enough to disrupt the environmental services that the forest provides and that could have knock on impacts in terms of the hydrological cycle and food security worldwide.

Of the different Brazilian States, we'll focus on those within Amazonia (see Fig. 3.7). There are three I would like to focus on:

Rondônia, which is the yellow area towards the West, and **Mato Grosso** north-east and then **Pará** state, north-east of that – these three areas are now heavily deforested and the combined effect during a drought period has the potential to seriously disrupt the rainfall cycle. I will describe that more when we look at the rainfall diagrams.

1. Ceará
2. Rio Grande do Norte
3. Paraíba
4. Pernambuco
5. Alagoas
6. Sergipe

Brazilian States, 1990

Figure 3.7

Figure 3.8 is a satellite photograph of the smoke formations over the forest and you can see one of the challenges here is that smoke prevents light and heat getting through to the canopy. And it is this light and heat energy which drives the evapo-transpiration process. So without high temperatures it cannot produce the magnitude of rains which enable the forest to flourish all the way along its 4,000 kilometre expanse westward, as well as providing moisture and energy to the Hadley Cell air circulation which takes it North, ultimately watering the grain belt of the US and beyond…a process known as teleconnection.

Figure 3.9 gives a slightly clearer picture. You can see the circled red areas. It is just so you can see where the fires are burning, as they are obscured by the smoke there. But they are prolific and on the right hand side you can see this slightly herringbone effect, the road goes vertically south to north and you have inroads into the Amazon with forest clearance on both sides of the road, this is typical of the way encroachment occurs.

57

Figure 3.8—Amazon headed towards permanent changes? Smoke from forest fires reduces rainfall and spells trouble for the Amazon, April 14th 2005

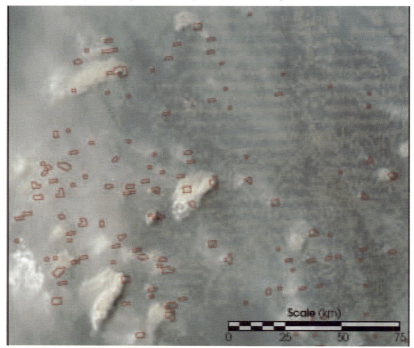

Figure 3.9

Precipitation Anomalies Dec-Feb 2007

(with respect to a 1961-1990 base period)

National Climatic Data Center/NESDIS/NOAA

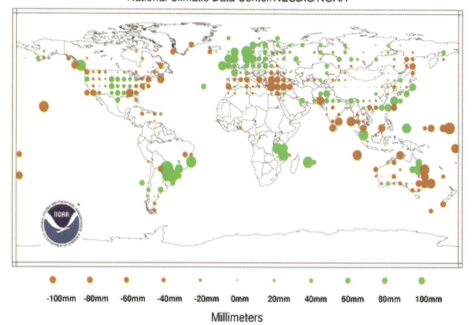

| -100mm | -80mm | -60mm | -40mm | -20mm | 0mm | 20mm | 40mm | 60mm | 80mm | 100mm |

Millimeters

Figure 3.10

Well this starts to get interesting now. Please glance back at *Figure 3.8* for a moment. This was taken in 2005 and 2005 was a particularly serious year for the Amazon because the rains failed in the early part of the season. They also did not come until quite late on in October and the Amazon suffered water-stress. Now it is built in a way to tolerate water stress – certainly a year of it – because of El Nino events which last for a year put it under that kind of strain, and it recovers during the following year. The challenge with 2006 was that again the rains failed and it was very slightly better than 2005, but not much. Now in 2007 (as you see in *Figure 3.10*) the rain is below average, but up to February it's been wet or normal…the areas we're interested in are on the eastern side of the Amazon basin.

The eastern side is most vulnerable – it's completely dependent on the Trade Winds coming from the tropical Atlantic. These easterlies (heading west) drive the rainfall cycle through the canopy, this happens in a series of hops. The rain falls and moisture is reabsorbed into cumulonimbus or thunderstorm clouds – which carry moisture hundreds of kilometres further West. Then rain it down again in as many as 7 micro-rainfall cycles feeding the entire forest as far West as the Andes.

Now a break in the forest, such as opening up in Rondônia, Mato Grosso and Pará, severs the east-west flow...the ability of the evapo-transpiration micro-cycles to feed the next swathe of forest. So there are two vulnerable points here. The recycling of rains westwards and with it the disruption of the feed to the teleconnection process I talked about earlier...not just feeding the grain belts of the North for example, but actually the whole of South America and Central America - Argentina for example depends on the Amazon for 50% of its rain – if the whole system starts to wane, 25% even 50% reductions in rainfall in these areas would not be unlikely...transforming the economies of these areas. The second vulnerable point is the eastern edge.

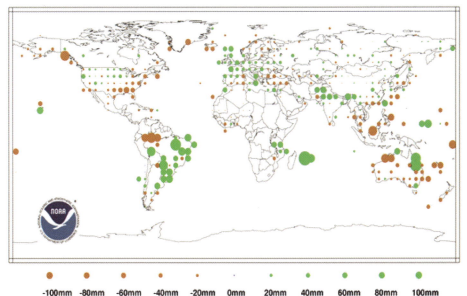

Figure 3.11

60

So February again we're looking at the eastern side of the basin and you can see the greening effect there. Lush, normal rainfall, we did well in February – I think most people were clapping their hands that low rainfall was not a long term trend and the drought had been broken – but as soon as we moved into March (See *Figure 3.12*) the dryness has returned again. That is unusual, dryer conditions would not be expected until the end of April.

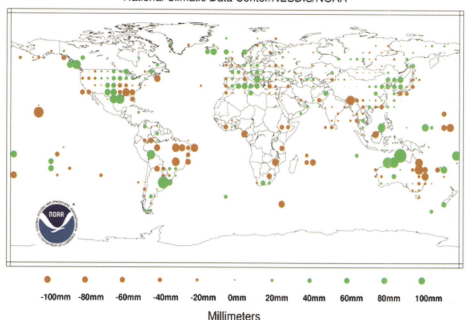

Figure 3.12

Precipitation Anomalies April 2007
(with respect to a 1961-1990 base period)
National Climatic Data Center/NESDIS/NOAA

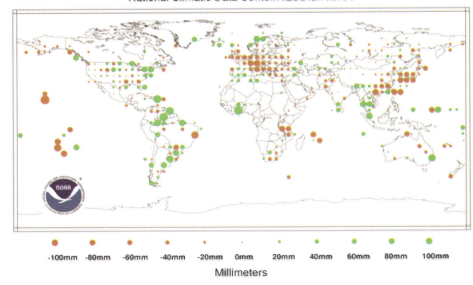

Figure 3.13

Dry conditions have returned at least a month early (Figure 3.13)

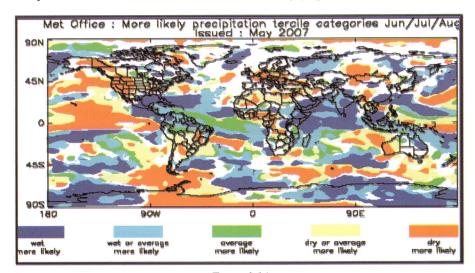

Figure 3.14

Figure 3.14 is a predictive Met Office map. If you look at the precipitation for June, July and August, again there is a risk of this season being a third, dryer than average season in parts of the forest and we have no idea of what the impacts will be by September/October. If the worst happens we could be having quite a different discussion regarding the imminence of climate disruption. There are no historic records of three consecutive seasons of drought in the Amazon and it has certainly not evolved to tolerate that.

Soil and Vegetation	WBGU	ICBP
Tropical Forests	428 Gt	553 Gt
Temperate Forests	159 Gt	292 Gt
Boreal Forests	559 Gt	395 Gt
Tropical Grasslands	330 Gt	326 Gt
Temperate Grasslands	304 Gt	199 Gt
Deserts/Semi-Deserts	199 Gt	169 Gt
Tundra	127 Gt	117 Gt
Croplands	128 Gt	169 Gt
Wetlands	225 Gt	n/a

Figure 3.15—Carbon Storage in the Terrestrial Biosphere

I wanted to give you an idea of how much carbon is locked up in tropical forests. These are two independent assessments of carbon sink data so lets look at mid-figures for tropical forests. In the region of 500 Gigatons. Remember we emit just 7 or 8 Gt from fossil fuel emissions and look at the havoc that's causing. There are astonishing amounts of carbon sitting in our tropical rainforests alone, of which 60% sits in the Amazon. So releasing that as a result of collapse would be a very big deal as far as climate change is concerned. In fact it would be fair to say it would put any future prospects of stabilising climate completely outside of our control. Now it would take several years, even a few decades for it to completely unfold, but once it started it would be almost irretrievable. You can't restore vast areas of mature forest, so there is no way of reabsorbing the carbon or returning humidity to the area.

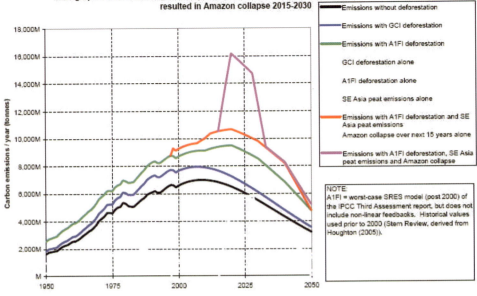

Figure 3.16

Now this takes a little bit of thought, so try to stay with me if you can. The base line, if you start down here, these are taken from the Contraction and Convergence model which of course we've been talking about through the All Party meetings here. The black line represents what implementing a Contraction and Convergence model could do for emissions i.e. getting fossil fuel emissions under control, and that is a potentially feasible position. That would be very positive. Add on to that the GCI position on deforestation – this is the blue line moving one up – it was predicted that from about the year 2000 we would probably have handled the deforestation issue and there wouldn't be any profligate deforestation of old growth forest from then on. Well clearly we have missed the boat on that one. We have had a spate of 7 years of the most serious deforestation, in excess of what we saw in the '80s and '90s.

Add on the third curve there, – A1F1 is the prediction from the Third Assessment Report from the IPCC. This curve (A1F1) is the more extreme likelihood of what deforestation would add to a stabilised emissions budget from fossil fuels. So bear in mind that we have handled the fossil fuels on the black line and now the green line shows what is happening if we don't handle deforestation, which we're not doing. So that is probably fairly true to reality. Except that it is worse. And it is worse because again the A1F1 index on the red line shows that when you add in the Asian peat emissions, and again this is primarily driven by the drive for palm oil again for the food and cosmetics industry, and now particularly in the last 18 months, the biofuels industry, is driving deforestation and peatland drainage for oil palm plantations and you can see just what happens to cumulative emissions on the red line.

This is incredibly serious because 20% of our emissions are now coming from this kind of land-use change. Now finally look at the pink line which is the potential for Amazonian collapse. We don't know when it would happen. There is already the looming risk of a sustained drought as described but climate models are more optimistic putting it a couple of decades away. These may be optimistic. No one predicted two years of drought and the possibility of a third. Partial dieback in the late Autumn would signal the start of another positive feedback accelerating climate change.

If it does occur we will see a very quick vertical assent on the pink line, an almost vertical trajectory and then it will slope off year on year as the forest burns itself out. In the Amazon alone we have a store of somewhere between 100 and 120 gigatons of carbon (combining forest and soil), well in excess of 10 times our annual emissions in the space of just a few years.

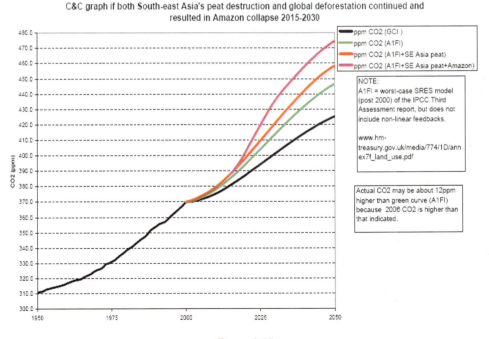

Figure 3.17

Figure 3.17 shows how it measures up in terms of concentrations. The coloured lines are breaking away from the black line meaning that carbon sinks are turning from sinks to sources of emissions and combined emissions spiralling out of control. All the discussion so far is dealing with reality - business as usual - fossil fuel burning out of control. These last two slides are saying that if we are able to control fossil fuels but not deforestation we will still cross the point where climate feedbacks will make our efforts irrelevant.

Solving the Deforestation Conundrum: Non-systemic v. Systemic Solutions

Well how do we solve this particular conundrum? I am calling it a conundrum because the panel dealing with this at the UNFCCC level, have shown themselves incapable of solving this. The drive for action regarding protecting old growth forests has been happening since the Earth Summit at Rio in 1992. So we have had around 15 years of ineffectiveness. One of the things that it comes down to is the difference in perspective between non-systemic and systemic understanding of the climate system. James Lovelock famously developed the GAIA hypothesis several decades ago, and it was one of the first systemic views of the earth, seeing it as a unified fully interacting system. If we had listened to him 4 decades ago, if we had listened to people like Fritz Schumacher in his early work, we would almost certainly not be in the severe position we're in now. Modern civilisation in contrast sees the Earth from a sectional view point, without reference to the broader picture and if we are to have any serious impact in terms of solving deforestation we really need to look at the bigger picture, i.e. recognising that we are now more likely to trigger runaway climate feedbacks as a result of ecosystem failure than we are as a result of profligate fossil fuel emissions.

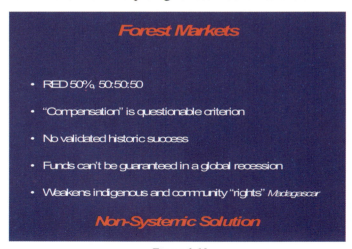

Figure 3.18

So here is another non-systemic solution currently on the table and, if early indications prove true, it is very likely to be validated for future UNFCCC policy in Bali this December. The new terminology for this is REDD or Reduced Emissions from Deforestation in Developing Countries and the suggestion put forward is that we reduce deforestation by 50%. Well I certainly wont be breathing a sigh of relief if we have legislation saying we can reduce deforestation by 50%, that will send emissions through the roof because as you imagine it is a licence for every country, every rainforest nation to fell the remaining 50% of their forests with impunity. This again is a serious example of non-systemic thinking. This is closely associated with the 50:50:50 position, which is to reduce the deforestation *rate* by 50% by 2050, thereby supposedly saving 50Gt of carbon... so effectively they are advocating we take 43 years to reduce the rate by 50%. I mean how much more ludicrous can it get? Non-systemic thinking shows itself as farcical.

The idea of compensation, this is what it is really all about. That market forces are used to compensate rainforest countries for not deforesting but it's not as simple as that. The funds don't really go to the people, it goes to the corporations and governments who are actually losing out as it were from not destroying the livelihoods and homes of millions of indigenous people. So the very idea of compensating for *not* violating human rights and *not* trashing the planet is a very questionable basis for funding. The Reduced Emissions from Deforestation is also dependent on vast funding streams coming through. If we had a global recession which any of these climate impacts could create, we face a position of not being able to sustain that funding. Defaulting on payment would in effect be

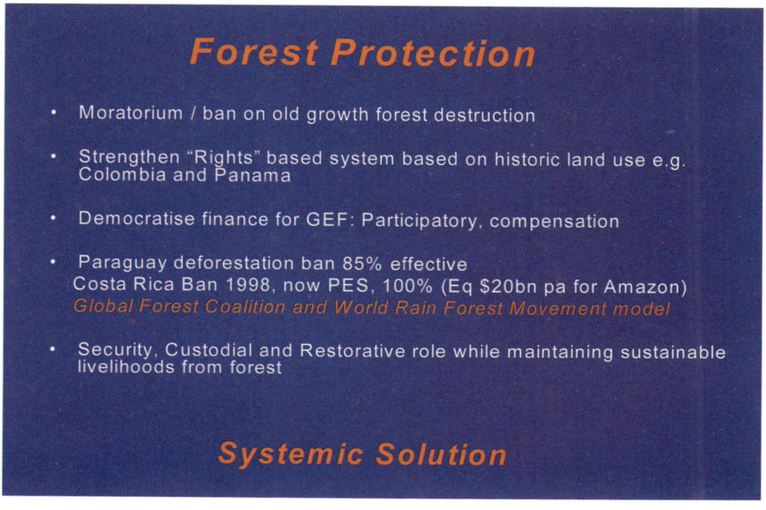

Figure 3.19

a license for deforestation. Finally, compensating anyone other than indigenous and local communities who live within and around the forest i.e. those who have historically safeguarded these areas, is to weaken their already tenuous land rights. Whoever receives the money is tacitly conferred with some historic right to the land. And if it's corporations and unscrupulous governments then don't be surprised if those living on the land get moved out.

OK just moving quite quickly through this, the systemic solutions are quite clear. We need a moratorium on old growth forest destruction for all our sakes, rainforest nations as well as the rest of the world. We need to be strengthening the rights of people who maintain the forest and could effectively implement security and even a restoration element. The Global Environment Facility could be very useful in this. There have been some modest successes there but it would have to be much more participatory and payments for these activities - safeguarding and restoring - will have to be a requirement. So money will certainly have to be involved. I am just suggesting that markets are not the ideal way to go about it. I won't go through them here but there have been some very effective results - Paraguay for example has reduced deforestation by 85% straight away by instituting a ban. That is very high. It is highly unlikely that a market mechanism could be this effective.

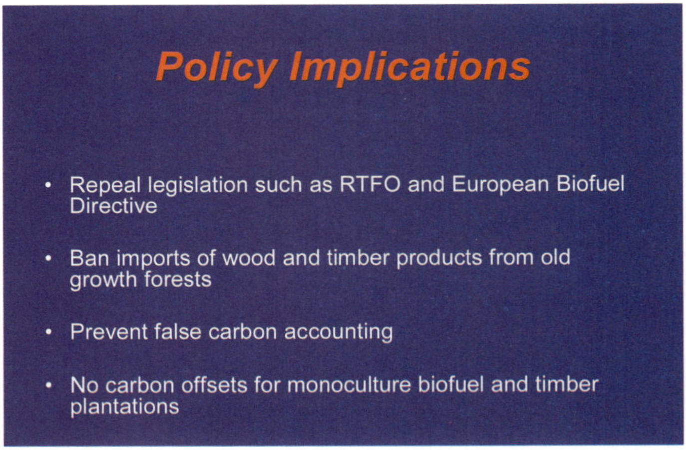

Policy Implications

- Repeal legislation such as RTFO and European Biofuel Directive

- Ban imports of wood and timber products from old growth forests

- Prevent false carbon accounting

- No carbon offsets for monoculture biofuel and timber plantations

Figure 3.20

The policy implications we have here for the UK are clear, certainly if I was to be more bold in terms of the Climate Bill. Let us re-examine legislation that we are currently engaged with – the Renewable Transport Fuels Obligation. Here we are trying to drive up biofuels production from under 1% of vehicle fuel, to 5%, the EU have legislated for 5.75% within three years. Those two pieces of legislation are driving deforestation, particularly in South East Asia and South America, this is *us, our role, our legislation*, that is part of the problem here.

We need to be careful about imports. And do we really want to be freeing up the WTO regulations which the UK are campaigning for at the moment? Very questionable. The false accounting, yes we might be reducing emissions from biofuels but the emissions are far greater overall - it is the global carbon accounting system we need to be looking at.

And last of all we can't be thinking of monoculture plantations for biofuels or timber anywhere in the world as being a carbon offset or attracting CDM credits. Even if plantations are on so called waste land or reclaimed land, monocultures which are biologically inert do not sustain themselves in the long term. In some cases they may accelerate climate change because they give off more carbon through the disturbance of soils. So those are the four key points that I would emphasise. Thank you for listening.

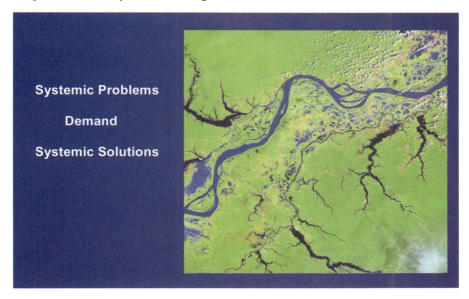

Figure 3.21

69

Presentation Four:
Feedbacks in Ice and Ocean Dynamics

Peter Wadhams

We have heard about the carbon feedbacks and the bio feedbacks related to deforestation. I am going to talk about some of the physical feedbacks that affect climate change and which are likely to speed it up in the manner of other positive feedbacks that we have heard about from Peter Cox. I will focus on feedbacks relating to the ocean and the atmosphere and especially the cold oceans.

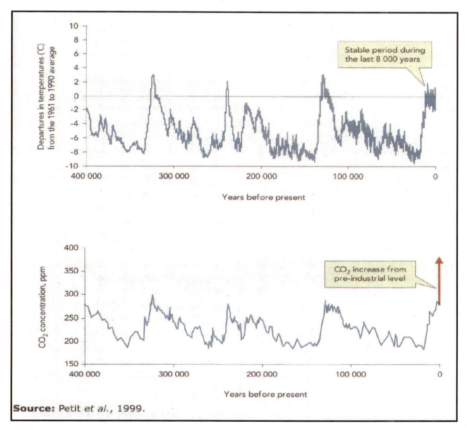

Source: Petit *et al.*, 1999.

Figure 4.1—reconstructed record of the global average temperature and atmospheric CO_2 concentration over the last 400,000 years.

We have already seen that the longest climate record that we know of, from Antarctic ice cores, shows that we have gone through a number of glacial cycles in the past half a million years, each of which causes the Earth's average temperature to follow a saw-tooth profile. Each glacial cycle also involves a cycling of the level of the carbon dioxide in the atmosphere, roughly in phase with the glaciation, but within clear limits of 200 ppm during glacial periods and 300 ppm during interglacials.

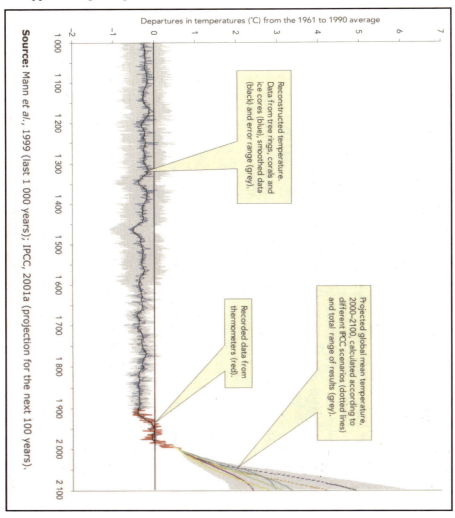

Figure 4.2—reconstructed and measured temperature over the last 1,000 years (northern hemisphere) and projected temperature rises in the next 100 years.

We have never gone above carbon dioxide concentrations of 300 ppm in the natural history of the half million years, but in recent years because of man's activities we are going right up into an unprecedented terrain of very high CO_2 levels. It is no accident that the curve of Earth's temperature during the past 1000 years – the classic "hockey stick" curve derived by Mann and Bradley – shows a sharp upturn since the Industrial Revolution which is far beyond the limits of recorded natural fluctuations. It is amusing to note that this curve has attracted a lot of specific criticism from one or two US senators that are not otherwise known for their scientific knowledge. The natural variability of climate over the last 1,000 years seems to be best represented by a very slow cooling, within a low range of variability, but then since the Industrial Revolution this has been replaced by an accelerating warming. We have got a deviation, the red line, which is definitely something other than the natural fluctuations which we have seen over the last thousand years. Of course the predictions based on the various climate models are taking us way beyond this up to a range of unprecedented possibilities.

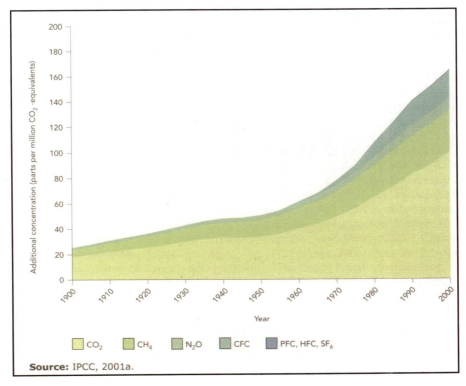

Figure 4.3—rise of greenhouse gases concentration compared with the year 1750

We should note that what is causing this is not entirely anthropogenic carbon dioxide. Already by 1900 we had more than 20 ppm (CO_2 equivalent) of additional greenhouse gases but today we are up to the 160 level. There are non-zero contributions from other greenhouse gases such as nitrous oxide and methane, and we should also note that CFCs are still present at quite high levels. So even though the Montreal Protocol dealt with certain CFCs as a cause of the ozone hole, the CFCs that have replaced them are still contributing to the greenhouse effect.

There are various models of the future growth of CO_2 levels, from the IPCC and other sources. (See *Figure 4.4*) There is a general consensus that to avoid disastrously rapid warming we must try to stop at 450 ppm, but it is difficult to see how this can be achieved when our emissions exceed natural absorption by such a wide margin (at present emissions are about double the rate of absorption of excess CO_2 by natural processes).

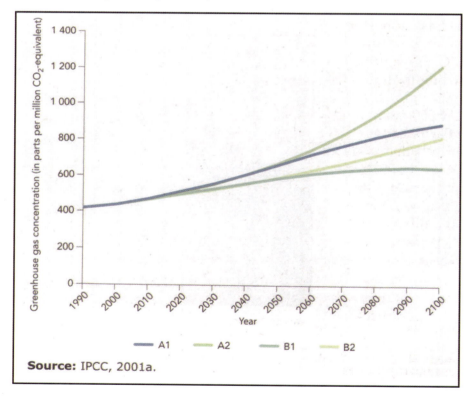

Figure 4.4—projected increase of GHG concentration in the atmosphere for four different possibility futures

ARTIC SEA ICE REDUCTION

There has been a dramatic decrease in arctic sea ice in the last two decades as indicated by:

- a **shrinking** of the boundaries, and
- a **thinning** of the interior ice cover

We have carried out ice thickness mapping from UK submarines since 1971 by agreement with the MoD.

We have found **thinning of 43% from the 1970s to 1990s** with an even more dramatic reduction in pressure ridge frequency. Latest data were acquired in 2004 and 2007 from HMS Tireless and show continued thinning.

Figure 4.5

Let us look at the first feedback which is relevant here, that may be increasing the rate of warming, and this is the sea ice reduction in the Arctic. There are two aspects to the change. There is a shrinking of the boundaries of the Arctic Ocean sea-ice and there is a thinning of the ice cover. The shrinkage is fairly easy to measure from satellites but the thinning is more difficult to measure and here Britain has been making a strong contribution. UK submarines have been going to the Arctic from 1971 onwards and, by collaboration with the Ministry of Defence, we have been able to go out on them and measure ice thickness during long transects across the whole ocean. In collaboration with American colleagues we have found that between the 1970s and the 1990s there has been a thinning of over 40% in mean thickness. The ridged ice, which contains the thickest components of the ice cover, has been reduced even more, by more than three-quarters. The last two data sets we got were in 2004 and March 2007, just three months ago, and this is useful and vital information because America stopped collecting this type of data in the year 2000.

Figure 4.6

Figure 4.6 is a picture of the most recent research in 2007, aboard HMS Tireless. I was measuring ice thickness right across the Arctic Ocean with a new type of multibeam sonar. Unfortunately we had an accident where we had an explosion of an oxygen generator and two of the sailors were killed. The slide shows the submarine surfaced in the ice after the accident - we had to find a place to come up through a polynya, an area of thin ice. We collected ice thickness data right up until the accident and this has shown a continuation of the thinning rate. We are now showing about 50% thinning of the ice cover since 25 years ago.

The ice thinning has serious implications, because it leads to a cut off point at which the ice-cover will actually disappear, at least in summer.

It won't disappear by shrinking from the sides, it will disappear by thinning and disappearing upwards so to speak. The shrinking of the ice area, which you can measure from satellites or aircraft, started in about 1950 and has proceeded at about 3-4% per decade. The thinning rate is much faster, so before the cover shrinks inwards and disappears it will disappear from thinning instead. This may occur as early as 2040 or even before.

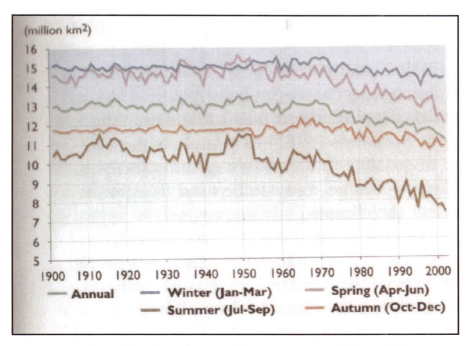

Figure 4.7 - observed seasonal Arctic sea-ice extent (1900 – 2003)

The implications are huge. Sea ice, by covering the sea surface with a solid sheet, essentially turns ocean into land from a climatic point of view. In the winter in the Arctic, the sea ice binds together the northern hemisphere land masses of Siberia and North America with the Arctic Ocean, and together they make a very large "land mass" that is sitting in the northern half of the world. But as soon as you remove the ice-cover and turn it into open ocean you are increasing evaporation, you are allowing light into the ocean and waves to be generated – you are basically replacing land by sea. The summer reduction of sea ice is now clearly visible from satellites. It is probably the clearest aspect of global warming that is visible from space. We can see that there are huge expanses now of the Beaufort Sea and the areas north of Russia which are ice-free in summer, which have never been before. So this not only results in increased evaporation, but also in a very much decreased average global albedo. When you have an ice or snow cover it reflects about 80%-90% of incident solar short-wave radiation straight back into space. But as soon as you take that ice cover away and replace it with ocean, the reflection goes down to about 10%. So we are absorbing a lot more radiation at the earth's surface and this is accelerating the rate of global warming.

Observed sea ice September 1979

Observed sea ice September 2003

Figure 4.8

These two images, constructed from satellite data, show Arctic sea ice concentrations in September, 1979 and 2003. September is the month in which sea ice is at its yearly minimum and 1979 marks the first year in which this data became available in meaningful form. The lowest sea ice concentration on record was in 2002.

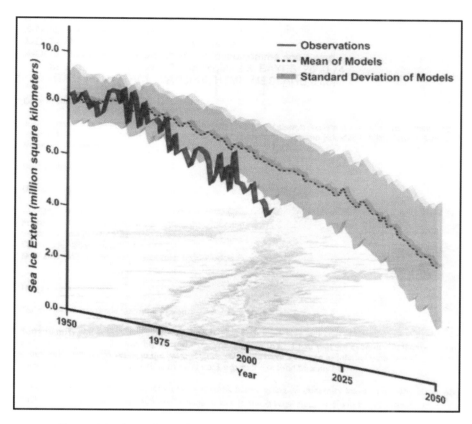

Figure 4.9 - Arctic September sea ice extent: observations and model runs

The rate of sea ice shrinking is now exceeding the predictions of most models. The grey band here shows the range of model predictions, while the black shows the observed shrinking rate of the sea ice in summer, so it is shrinking faster than expected.

In Figure 4.10 (over), looking at all regions of the Arctic, we see the blue is the mean thickness of the ice cover as it was in the '70s, the green is as it was at the end of the '90s, and it has gone on thinning since. The critical point here will be when the total growth in the winter is no greater than the total melt in the summer and this is what happens at the moment in Antarctica, which has a seasonal ice cover. As soon as the summer melt exceeds the winter growth then you do away with the ice in the summer and you will have open water.

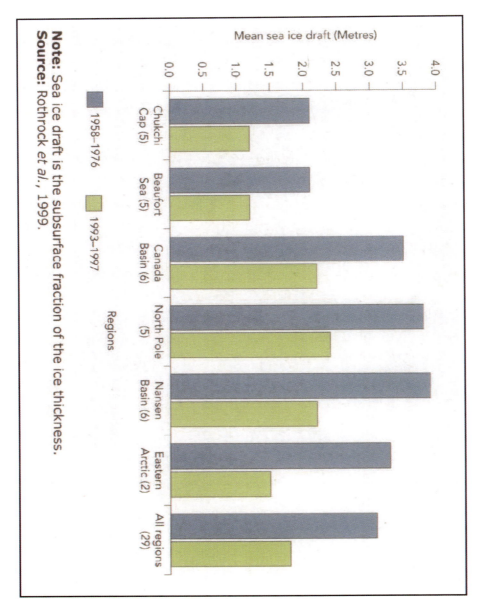

Figure 4.10 - regional changes of mean sea ice draft in the Arctic

80

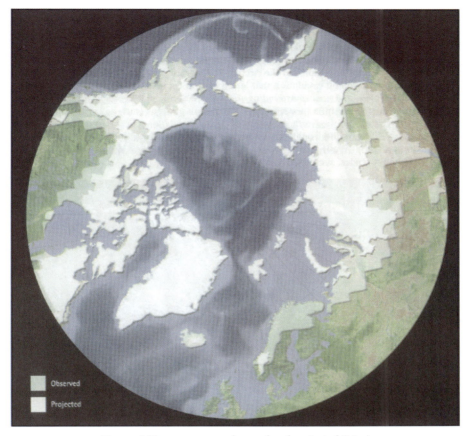

Figure 4.11 - snow cover observed and projected (May)

Adding to this feedback is the fact that as the climate warms, the snow cover in winter also decreases. In this slide the white is what we expect to see as the winter snow extent by late this century, while the grey is what we have now in winter. Large swathes of snow lying on land will go, and this enhances the albedo feedback effect. The only good thing about see ice shrinkage is that it will improve navigation around the Arctic. The north-west passage around the north of Canada is likely to stay choked in summer, but the northern sea route, the north-east passage around the north of Siberia, will become navigable. It is already ice-free in most summers except for the one narrow Vilkitsky Strait, and you can now almost guarantee to be able to sail through it. This will increase access to Japan by sea, cutting the sea voyage by some 6000 km, and will increase access to off-shore oil and gas.

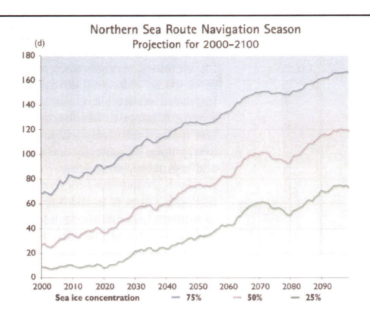

Northern Sea Route Navigation Season
Projection for 2000–2100

(d)

Sea ice concentration   — **75%**   — **50%**   — **25%**

Observed Sea Ice Cover
September 16, 2002

     Figure 4.12

Figure 4.13 - Greenland ice sheet melt extent

One effect of the reduction in sea ice is that you are exposing the coasts of previously ice-girt landmasses to a warmer atmosphere and this results, in the case of Greenland, in surface melting in summer, which never used to occur. These satellite pictures show how much of the surface area of Greenland now shows some sign of melt in the summer. This has grown greatly and we are now seeing a definite loss of ice every year from the Greenland ice-sheet.

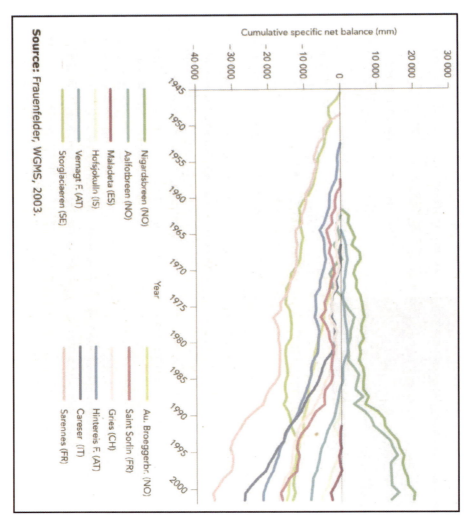

Figure 4.14 - cumulative net balance of glaciers from all European glacier regions

Mountain glaciers in the northern hemisphere are now almost all retreating. The only ones that are expanding are a few in southern Norway which are gaining from the increased warm moist air that is reaching them from the Atlantic.

The contribution of ice sheet loss to global sea levels is something which has been guessed at, but the problem in making good predictions is that the element that is missing is Antarctica. We can predict for instance that the melt rate of the Greenland ice-sheet alone will add 4 cm. to global sea levels by the end of the

84

century, while the melt of glaciers in general will add about 50% to the roughly 60 cm that has been forecast for the effect of warming of the ocean alone. However, as measurements in Antarctica are so difficult we do not know what its contribution will be, and this leaves us with a wide range of uncertainty for overall predicted global sea level rise. Thus we can say that probably the least good predictions of global warming models are their predictions of how much sea-level rise we are going to see, and it is very critically dependent on whether

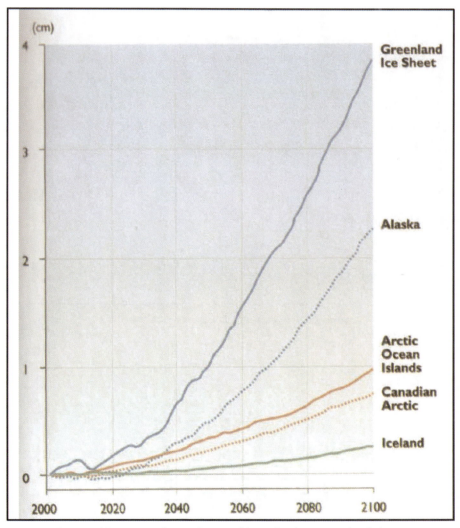

Figure 4.15 - projected contribution of Arctic land ice to sea level change

the polar ice-sheets start to melt or not. So far this seems to be happening with Greenland but not yet with Antarctica.

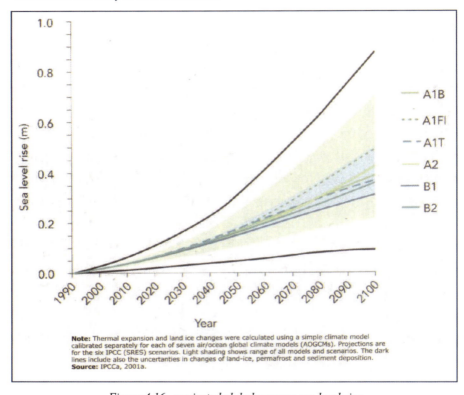

Figure 4.16 - projected global average sea level rise

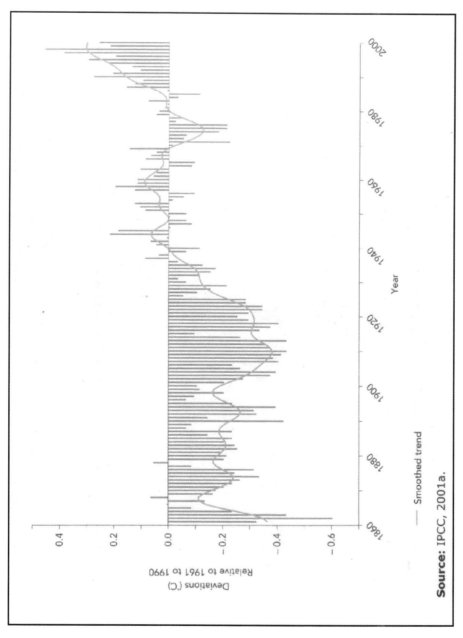

Figure 4.17 - annual sea surface temperature (SST) deviations averaged over the northern hemisphere

The thing of which we are certain is that the sea surface temperature is rising globally, and this is decreasing the density of sea water and causing the ocean to stand higher.

One example of ocean warming has been locally here in the North Sea. The North Sea winter temperatures have gone up by more than a degree in the last few decades and this is one of the reasons why the cod is disappearing from the North Sea because it is becoming too warm for cod to spawn.

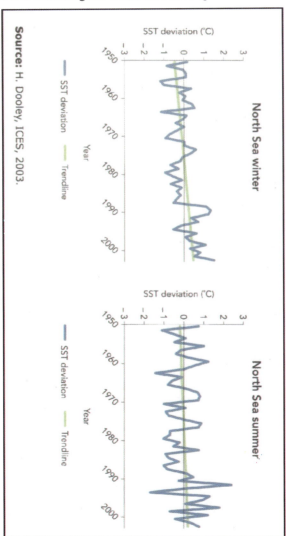

Figure 4.18 - deviation of winter and summer surface temperatures in the North Sea

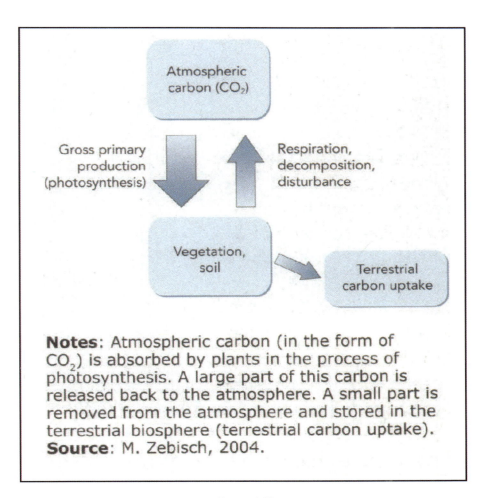

Notes: Atmospheric carbon (in the form of CO_2) is absorbed by plants in the process of photosynthesis. A large part of this carbon is released back to the atmosphere. A small part is removed from the atmosphere and stored in the terrestrial biosphere (terrestrial carbon uptake). **Source**: M. Zebisch, 2004.

Figure 4.19

The carbon balance has already been mentioned.

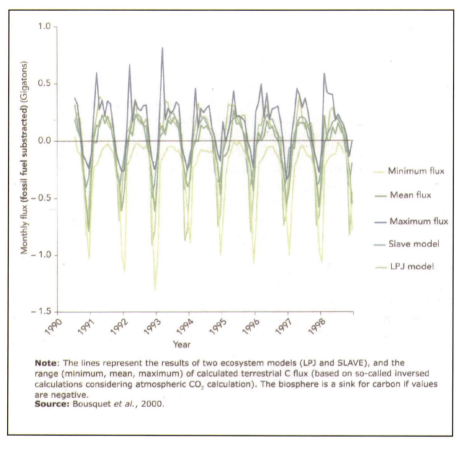

Figure 4.20 - inter-annual variation in European carbon fluxes from the biosphere to the atmosphere

Figure 4.20 shows work done by the European Environment Agency on Europe as a sink or a source for carbon fluxes. Their carbon analysis shows that Europe is becoming less of a carbon sink for the biosphere than it used to be. This means that a greater proportion of our carbon emissions remain in the atmosphere.

90

rce: CRU, 2003; Jones and Moberg, 2003.

Figure 4.21 - observed annual, winter and summer temperature deviations in Europe

We know that the temperatures in Europe are also going up at an increased rate, and the slide shows what has been happening since 1980. One of the things that may slow this warming down for western Europe, peculiarly enough, is ocean convection.

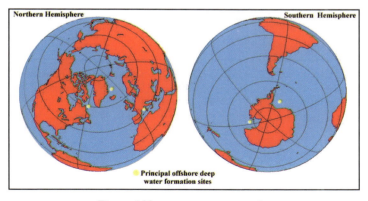

Figure 4.22 - open ocean convection

91

Deep open ocean convection only occurs in a handful of places. Not only does deep convection affect the properties of the deep waters, but it also affects the carbon cycle and oceanic circulation through its role in the thermohaline circulation. Thermohaline circulation helps maintain the flow of warm surface waters to high latitudes, and as a result northern Europe has an unusually mild climate for its latitude.

We know that there is a thermohaline circulation or a global conveyor belt – which is the slow long term circulation of the ocean, not driven by the wind but driven by temperature and salinity changes caused by precipitation and uneven heating of the ocean surface. This conveyor belt is a combination of surface currents and a return flow of deep currents, with the two being connected by regions of sinking, or convection. The warm current coming up to Europe, a part of the Gulf Stream, is one of the surface currents. This sinks at two critical locations which act as the "pulleys" of the conveyor belt. One is in the Greenland Sea and one in the Labrador Sea. In addition there is a convective site that is not very important in the Mediterranean, and a couple in the Antarctic.

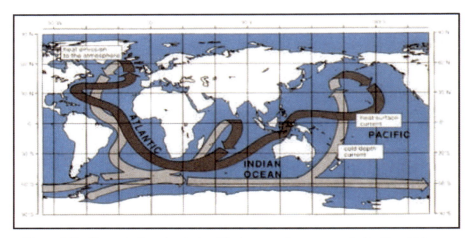

Figure 4.23 - Thermohaline circulation. The large marine conveyor belt with cold deep flow and warm surface current (Source: DKRZ/MPI-Hamburg)

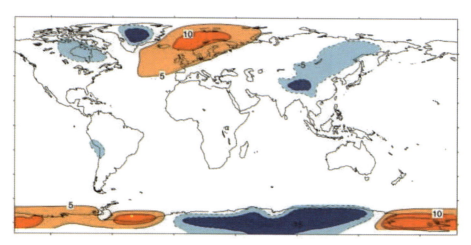

Figure 4.24 - Thermohaline circulation. Annual mean surface temperature anomalies, from NCAR data, relative to zonal averages. There is a 5-10°C warm anomaly over NW Europe and the Nordic Seas (Rahmstorf, S.A., Ganapolski, 1999)

My lab has been working in the Greenland Sea in the middle of winter for several years measuring the convection, and we found that it occurs in the form of very narrow "chimneys", that is, rotating cylinders of water sinking from the surface to the deep ocean.

There is a chimney in the oceanographic section shown (next page), and a computer view of the cylinder is also shown (coloured red, page 95).

Chimneys results from ice formation in the middle of the Greenland Sea in a particular area which is a kind of tongue of ice, called Odden in Norwegian, which you can see on the top right. The trouble is that since 1998 this tongue has ceased to form in winter. It used to grow every single winter, and each time it forms the salt that is rejected from the ice formation increases the surface water density and allows the deep convection which occurs as chimneys. Since 1998 the only chimneys we see are one or two that are just hanging on and surviving rather than new ones forming. The result of this reduction in sinking is that there is going to be a slow down of the thermohaline circulation, a slow down of this conveyor belt, and this will produce a cooling, or at least a reduction in the rate of warming, of the north east Atlantic. The projections of climate models which take partial account of this are that this will shield north-west Europe from some of the effects of global warming.

Figure 4.25 (over) - Sea ice and convection (appears on pages 94 and 95): We have dis-covered that the convection in the Greenland Sea occurs through narrow (cont. p. 95)

Sea ice and convection

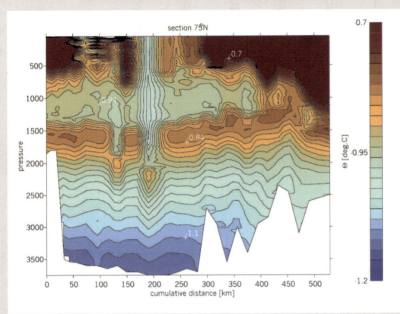

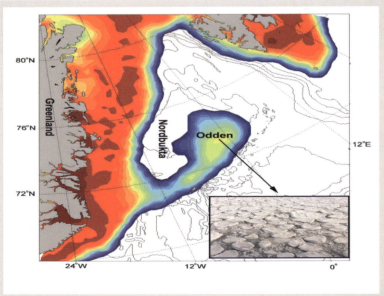

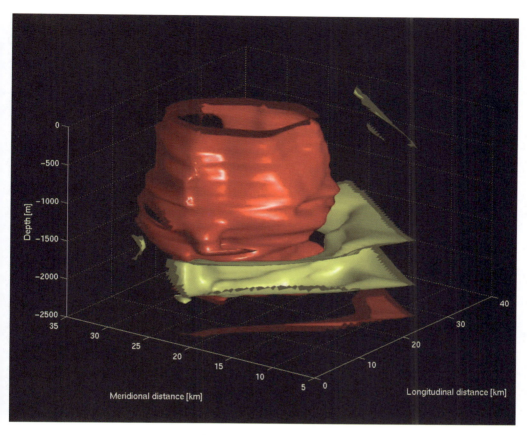

Figure 4.25 (continued)

(cont. from p. 93) columns called CHIMNEYS. They can only form because of salt added at the surface through ice formation over a tongue shaped region in winter. Since 1998 this has not occurred, so no new chimneys are forming.

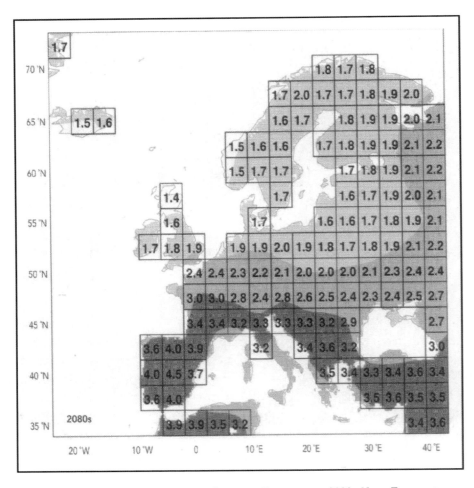

Figure 4.26 - projected temperature changes in Europe up to 2080. Note: Temperature change (°C). Relative to average temperature in the period 1961-1990. Intermediate ACA-CIA scenario in a broad range of possible future emissions. Source: IPCC, 2001b; Parry et al., 2000

The prediction shown comes from such an intermediate scenario, and we see that the predicted temperature rise this century in Britain and Norway and north-west Europe, anywhere exposed to the Atlantic Ocean, is down one or two degrees, but if we are looking at the Mediterranean countries it is very much higher, three to four degrees.

This is also accompanied, for Spain and Italy, by big reductions in rainfall, of 30% or more. We are looking, in fact, at the possible evolution of southern

96

Europe into a full North African-type desert climate and the effects of this will be disastrous.

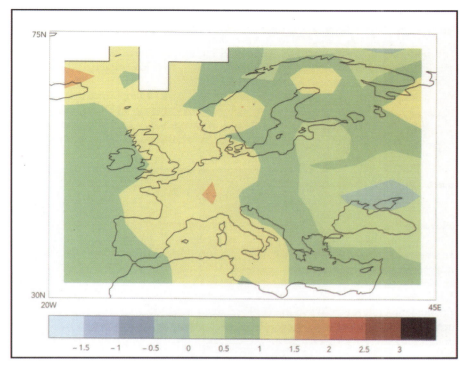

Figure 4.27 - Annual temperature deviation in Europe in 2003. Relative to average temperature from 1961-1990 (°C). Source: CRU, 2003; Jones and Moberg, 2003.

Even a tiny effect like the very warm summer that happened in Europe in 2003 produced several thousand deaths in France. (See *Figure 4.28, over*)

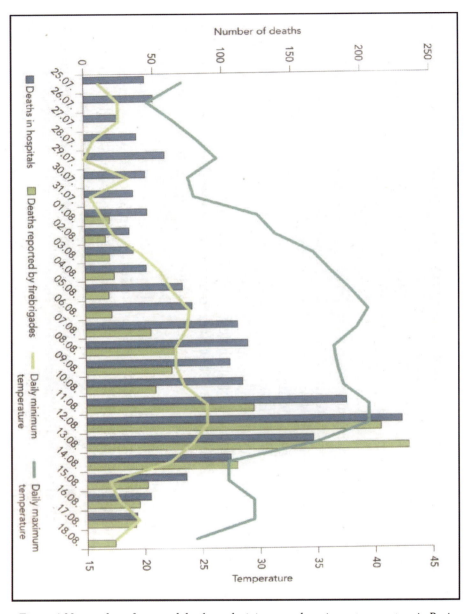

Figure 4.28 - number of reported deaths and minimum and maximum temperature in Paris during the heatwave in summer 2003. Source: IVS, 2003

If we look at the left hand axis (of Figure 4.28) we see the daily death rate in Paris in the summer of 2003. It lagged the air temperature by about a week, so people were getting overheated and dying within a week, or their bodies were being found within a week. So here we see a minor effect, in a civilised country, yet still one which caused a large number of deaths.

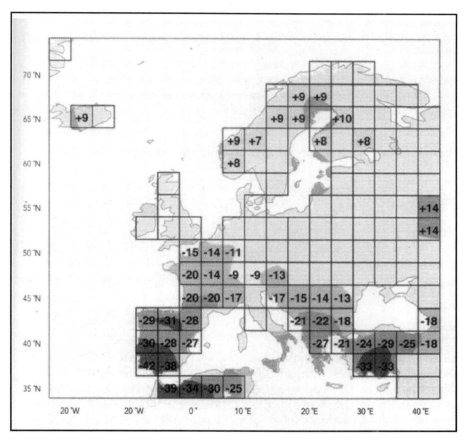

Figure 4.29– projected change in summer precipitation in Europe up to 2080. % change relative to average precipitation in the period 1961-1990. Intermediate ACACIA scenario in a broad range of possible future emissions. Source: IPCC, 2001b; Parry, et al, 2000.

If we look at rainfall predictions the models predict little change, even a small increase, in Scandinavia, but again a very large decrease in southern Europe, and we can see that Spain, which is already going up by about 4 degrees in temperature, going down by about 30% in rainfall, which means it is essentially turning into a desert. So we are seeing the North African climate moving into southern Europe.

OCEAN ACIDIFICATION

The oceans are absorbing carbon dioxide (CO_2) from the atmosphere and this is causing chemical changes by making them more acidic (that is, decreasing the pH of the oceans). In the past 200 years the oceans have absorbed approximately half of the CO_2 produced by fossil fuel burning and cement production. Calculations based on measurements of the surface oceans and our knowledge of ocean chemistry indicate that this uptake of CO_2 has led to a reduction of the pH of surface seawater of 0.1 units, equivalent to a 30% increase in the concentration of hydrogen ions.

If global emissions of CO_2 from human activities continue to rise on current trends then the average pH of the oceans could fall by 0.5 units (equivalent to a three fold increase in the concentration of hydrogen ions) by the year 2100. This pH is probably lower than has been experienced for hundreds of millennia and, critically, this rate of change is probably one hundred times greater than at any time over this period. The scale of the changes may vary regionally, which will affect the magnitude of the biological effects.

(Source: Royal Society policy document 12/05)

Two key questions

Climate change involves a complex set of feedback processes which may amplify one another, e.g. sea ice retreat leads to lower global albedo leads to more retreat, warmer high latitudes lead to ice sheet melt leading to accelerated sea level rise, etc.

We must be concerned about two things:

1. Can feedbacks on-feedbacks lead to accelerated warming or accelerated rise in CO_2 levels for any given rise in emissions, i.e. will each unit of carbon that we emit cause a bigger effect in the future than it does now?

2. Are these feedbacks also likely to cause a reduction in the fraction of man-added carbon (currently about half) that is removed from the atmosphere by natural processes e.g. seabed deposition, absorption in ocean and in biomass production? This would make our emissions reduction target more stringent.

There are one or two wild cards which I don't have time to talk about, but one that has been mentioned a lot very recently is acidification of the ocean. As additional carbon dioxide that has been put into the atmosphere by man dissolves in the ocean it increases the acidity of the ocean, i.e. its hydrogen-ion concentration (called pH). This has gone down by about 0.1 of a unit of pH in the last few decades and on present rate of change it will go down by another 0.5 in the next 100 years. This creates another positive feedback. One of the ways that carbon is removed permanently from the ecosystem is that it gets incorporated into the shells of plankton. The plankton die, the shells drop to the ocean bed and become part of the sediments, and you can forget about them for a long time.

With the acidification of the ocean it may be that first of all the shells will start to dissolve as they sink, or that there will be a reduction in the production of shell material by plankton. This is a massive problem if it happens because it is a massive disruption of the marine ecosystem and also of course a loss of one of the sinks that we have been relying on for getting rid of half of the carbon dioxide that we are putting into the atmosphere.

We have not only got to reduce our emissions, but we have got to be concerned that some of the sinks that have been doing part of the job for us are themselves getting to be less efficient or even ceasing to act.

Summary

So that is really my message which really just amplifies the message that we have had from the previous speakers. The anthropogenic emissions of greenhouse gases into the atmosphere produce feedbacks which unfortunately all tend to be positive ones. As warming occurs these feedbacks act either to reduce the natural carbon sinks that we have, or to increase the rate at which carbon dioxide levels rise in the atmosphere per unit of emission. Therefore you can get an accelerated rate of carbon dioxide level rise in the atmosphere, even though we may not be increasing the rate at which we are putting it into the atmosphere ourselves. This is a strong argument in favour of achieving much more stringent reductions in carbon emissions than hitherto contemplated, so as to compensate for some of these delayed feedback effects as well as the direct and immediate effect of the gases on the climate system.

Presentation Five:

Accelerated Climate Change and the Task of Stabilisation

David Wasdell

This is by way of a summary of the overall situation that has been outlined so far. Most of the systems known to affect climate change are in net positive feedback.

> **Most of the systems known to affect climate change are now in net positive feedback. Each feedback mechanism accelerates its own specific process. As a whole, the complex adaptive feedback system consists of an interactive set of mutually reinforcing subsystems.**

Technically we use positive feedback to talk about bad things and negative to talk about good things. Let's talk about accelerating feedbacks and damping feedbacks shall we. Most of the feedbacks are accelerating climate change. Each mechanism in its own process accelerates the effect of that process. But as we started looking at the overall conceptual modelling of the feedback system we began to realise the outputs of one feedback are the inputs to all the others, particularly when they are temperature sensitive. So they begin to work together and accelerate each other. Extra heating because of the carbon cycle creates a situation where the ice cycle is accelerated. Less albedo reflection increases the warming, which increases all the other things that are temperature-dependent. So it is an interactive set of mutually reinforcing systems.

> **The second order feedback system therefore accelerates the rate of climate change.**

I shall never forget (to Peter Wadhams) sitting in your study in Cambridge, when you said, "David I think you have just put your finger on something that nobody has spotted before". That we have what we call a second order feedback system. Feedback on feedback that accelerates climate change. And that faces us with the possibility of what has been called "The Tipping Point" in the whole earth system.

Now tipping points are rapidly becoming buzz words and YouTube words. We have tipping points in our giving up of smoking and all sorts of things. But a tipping point occurs when a system's behaviour gets to a threshold and then moves past that threshold into behaviours from which it does not easily return. It accelerates away from equilibrium. If we go beyond the point, not just where natural systems pass that threshold, but where natural and human systems together reach the point where human intervention can no longer return the system to base, then we precipitate runaway climate change. That will set off a major extinction event, like the five massive extinctions and crises in the whole biosphere that we have so far experienced in the geological history. That now is being seen as a very real possibility.

So what is a tipping point? Figure 5.1 is quite a good example of it.

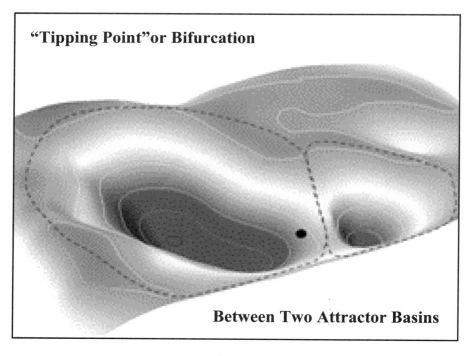

Figure 5.1

Here you have what is called an 'attractor basin' where behaviours are held stably in a zone which may go to ice ages and inter-glacial warm periods, but it stays within that envelope of possibilities. What the Industrial Revolution has done has pushed with the feedbacks and the forcings up to a ridge, a watershed if you will, and pushed us just into the beginnings of accelerated change that can take us out of that traditional attractor basin, and push us into a hotter earth scenario. It would indeed be contained eventually, probably by massive cloud formation and would not go as far as the Venus answer of very, very hot earth. The last time Peter Wadhams and I discussed this, he said, "I think we should look at that again David, because I am not quite certain where these boundaries occur!"

So that is an example of a tipping point, or bifurcation. It is a bifurcation if you are walking along the ridge because you can go either way. It is a tipping point if you are coming up and over the watershed into a new basin.

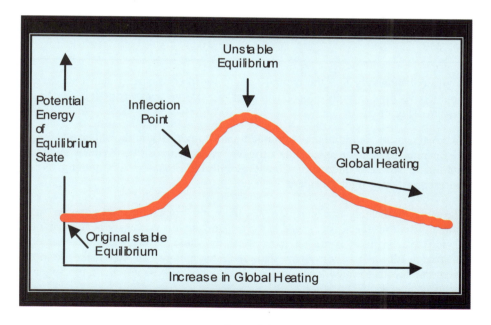

Figure 5.2

This represents the cross section through this watershed zone between the two attractor basins. To the left lies the old stable equilibrium, the ice-ages and the inter-glacial warm periods. Then comes an inflection point where positive feedbacks begin to start acting. That leads on to the unstable equilibrium, where amplifying feedbacks just outweigh the containing feedbacks and the whole

105

system is very unstable – is it going to go this way, is it going to go that way. As we go on increasing positive feedback, it goes over the top of the hill, and leads to the beginnings of accelerated change and potentially runaway global heating.

That is the natural system. Now I want to couple that with the human system. I will introduce this slowly, it is a complicated concept and I find difficulty explaining it, let alone other people understanding it. What we are looking at here is the **critical threshold** where as a species we lose control of the runaway process.

Introducing the concept of "Critical Threshold"

- **the point beyond which the power of positive feedback overwhelms the capacity for human intervention**
- **the point at which the cost of stabilisation escalates asymptotically towards infinity**

If you put humanity and the natural system together as one system then there would be a tipping point where whatever we do, we can't stop it happening anymore (Figure 5.3).

So down near the origin in the bottom left hand corner back in the old equilibrium area, increased global heating didn't trigger very much positive feedback and we had lots of power to intervene. Climate stabilisation cost virtually nothing, as is represented by the light-green area.

The more the heating has increased, the more the temperature has gone up, the more positive feedback is engaged in the system, the less power we have to act on it, until we begin to approach the critical threshold. Here there is so much positive feedback in the system that the interventions we can make do not overcome the accelerated feedback. At that point we lose control and precipitate runaway change.

In fact as we approach the critical threshold, it is not just that it costs more to make the intervention or takes more intervention to make the difference. The cost actually goes off to infinity. It is an asymptotic line here. We cross that threshold at our peril.

Now let's combine the two graphs in one. We think we are just on the right side of the unstable equilibrium, the point where positive feedback starts accelerating the climate beyond the instability and towards the critical threshold. Stern

106

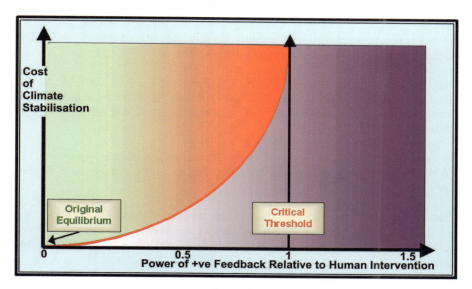

Figure 5.3

recognised that the sooner we intervene, the lower would be the economic cost of climate stabilisation. He did not recognise that there is a limit to the timescale beyond which intervention is impossible. So this really does turn the economics

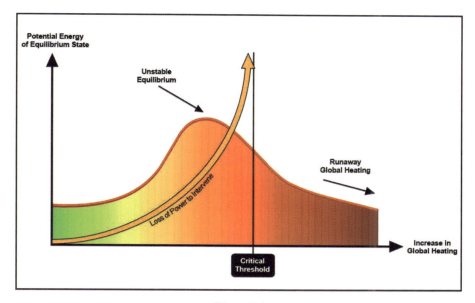

Figure 5.4

beyond which intervention is impossible. So this really does turn the economics on its head.

Only yesterday, I was talking to the First Secretary of the Swedish Embassy in Ottawa. He said, "It is no longer a question of can we afford it. It is a question of can we do it. Then we have to cut our economics to fit the imperative from the environment."

So economic imperatives are no longer the driver of climate policy. The environment drives the policy and the policy has to cut its economics to fit the cloth of the environmental system.

That is a huge shift strategically in our understanding of climate change and has not been taken into account in Kyoto. It has not been taken into account in European legislation. It has not been taken into account in the current Bill before Parliament.

Now I want to introduce the time dimension to this diagram (see Figure 5.5 opposite). We have had to rotate it a bit so that the camera angles show up the various pathways through the landscape. On the left face is the picture I had before. The green valley represents the old equilibrium area where it was safe enough, and climate was stable within limits. Running from lower left to upper right is the ridge of unstable equilibrium. Beyond the ridge is the runaway potential of the system moving into a heated area and out of control. The critical threshold is represented by the wall, the wall beyond which we must not pass if we are to have any hope of re-stabilising the climate. Business as usual takes us over the hill and through that wall into a catastrophe. Current Kyoto strategy slows it down a bit, but we end up in the same place.

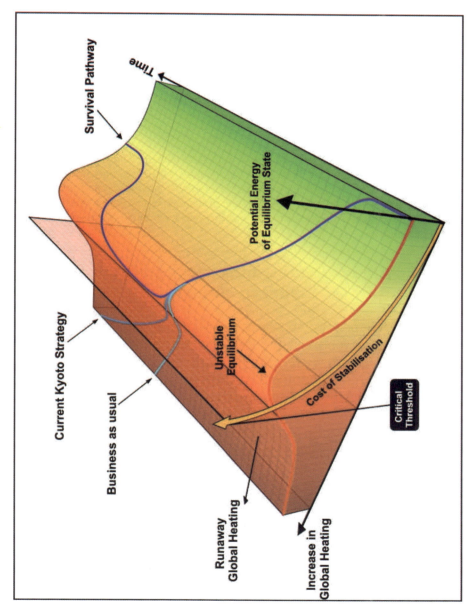

Figure 5.5

The intervention that is required is one that slows down the feedback system, slows down the rise in temperature and holds us this side of the critical threshold until the temperature rise stops. By that time temperature-driven feedback ceases to be a problem. The intervention that we will have made by then will bring us back over the hill and into an equilibrium temperature.

Climate will have been stabilised. Runaway climate change will have been prevented. The extinction event will have been avoided. The stable equilibrium temperature may, however, still be too high to avoid dangerous, even catastrophic, climate change.

We are now in the early stages of runaway climate change. There is no naturally occurring negative feedback process. When Dennis Meadows, one of the authors of the Club of Rome's Limits to Growth, worked with me on some of this earlier in this process, he said 'we have to look for some big negative feedbacks to contain this system', but they are not out there to be found. We have to make them ourselves.

We are now in the early stages of runaway climate change

- There does not appear to be any naturally occurring negative feedback process in place to contain its effects
- Strategically we have to generate a negative feedback intervention of sufficient power to overcome the now active positive feedback process
- Then maintain its effectiveness during the period while temperature-driven feedback continues to be active

---

So strategically we have to generate a negative feedback, a damping intervention of sufficient power to overcome the already active accelerating feedbacks, and maintain its effectiveness during that period while temperature driven feedback threatens to destabilise it and push it beyond the wall. That is one extraordinarily difficult intervention. I do not personally believe it is impossible, as some doomsters say, but it certainly is out of all keeping with the strategies currently in place. In order to focus on the new strategic task we now face, I will introduce a different way of looking at the material, namely the perspective of "Radiative Forcing".

Radiative Forcing

Radiative Forcing is the difference between energy that comes in from the sun and the energy we radiate back out again. At the moment we are pushing out about 1% less than we are receiving, that is what is causing the problem. We are moving away from radiative balance (the equilibrium position with no global heating) and increasing the amount of excess heat that we are holding year by year.

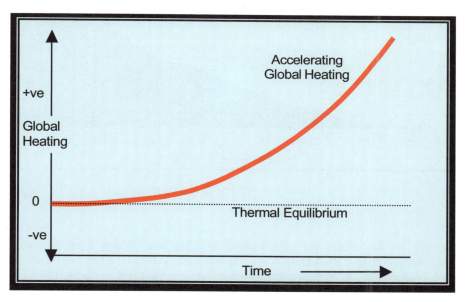

Peter Cox has shown us something like Figure 5.7 already, so I will move through it quite quickly. Here are the contributions to radiative forcing – global heating – from four different sources, up to the year 2000. Firstly from methane, which has levelled off at the moment. That is largely because we have shifted from coal-fired to gas-fired power stations, we have started to deal with outputs from landfill, we have plugged the leaks in gas pipes, and we have stopped venting methane into the atmosphere from the oil fields. As the feedbacks in the methane system increase, we would expect this to begin to go up again over the coming decades.

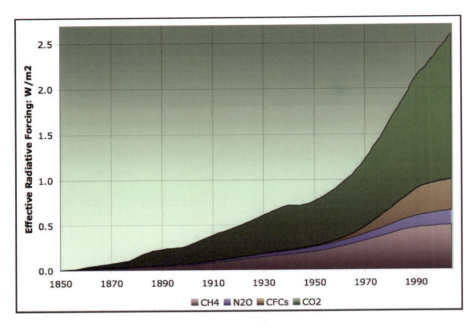

Figure 5.7

Nitrous oxides, a product of extensive fertiliser use, though small are still increasing. That is another area in which we can intervene. Emission of CFCs has been cut off, following implementation of the Montreal Protocol, but they stay in the atmosphere for a long time so their effect on global heating will only slowly degrade. The major contributor, of course, is carbon dioxide.

The next slide (Figure 5.8) is taken from the work of Jim Hansen and others at the Gifford Institute of Space Studies at NASA. It provides a summary of all the different contributors to global heating apart from low altitude water vapour, and change in albedo. Carbon dioxide, at the year 2000, drove radiative forcing of 1½ watts per square metre; methane about half a watt; CFCs about one-third of a watt; the nitrogen oxides just over a tenth. Ozone – at the very high levels in the atmosphere it is a slight coolant, but low level ozone is adding about four-tenths of a watt per square metre. A bit of water vapour at high altitude is produced by the breakdown of methane.

Here is a new one: – **black carbon**. It is generated by the burning of Biomass, the incomplete combustion of fossil fuels, and industrial processes. Sooty particles of black carbon are released which then absorb heat and warm the

112

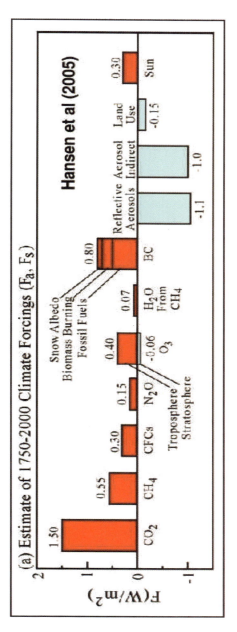

Figure 5.8

atmosphere. It also settles on the surface of ice and snow and makes it more absorbent of heat and light energy, so it reduces the albedo of the snow areas. There are blackening areas in the snow of the northern hemisphere from the huge industrial explosion in China. **Aerosols** – the sulphate particles also scatter light energy and reflect it back, so they are coolants. This is global dimming from the particulates. They also have an indirect effect by creating extra cloud cover which also reflects out light. **Land use**, deforestation increases albedo, leading to slight cooling. Finally, **sun** has increased its energy outputs a little during this period, though there has been a slight decrease since 1987, the years in which the fastest global warming has occurred. So if we take those last 5 items and add them together for convenience, we have a negative radiative forcing of about 1 watt per square metre.

Now we put this into graphical form (Figure 5.9). We stayed in radiative balance (no global warming) until the start of the industrial revolution, then it began to increase. By the year 2000, CO_2 on its own was contributing 1½ watts per square metre.

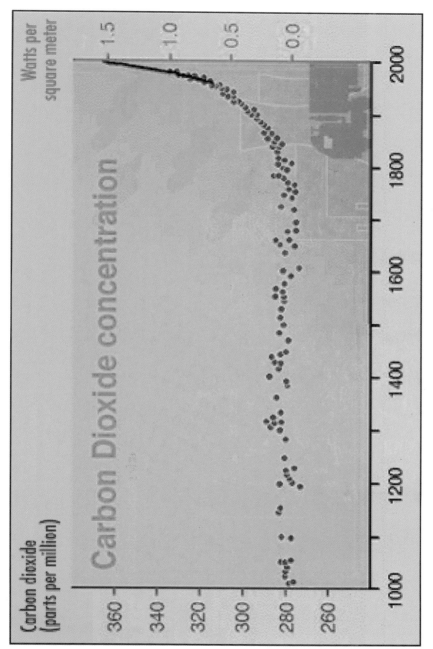

Figure 5.9

By 2007, CO_2 concentration had risen to 382 ppm, adding another 0.3 watt per square metre. Add in CO_2 equivalents, nitrous oxide, methane, CFCs, and ozone, and the concentration rises to about 445 ppm CO_{2e}.

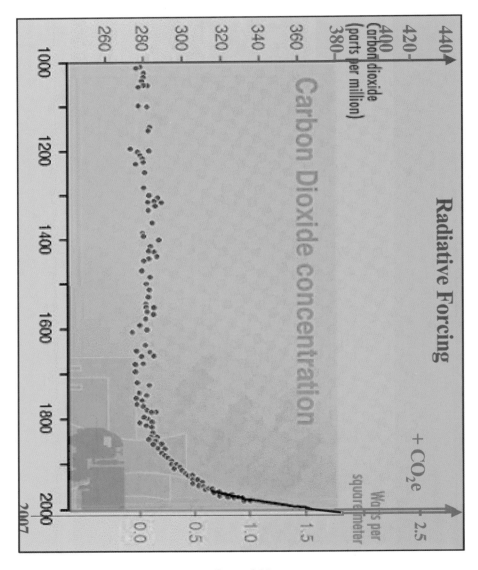

Figure 5.10

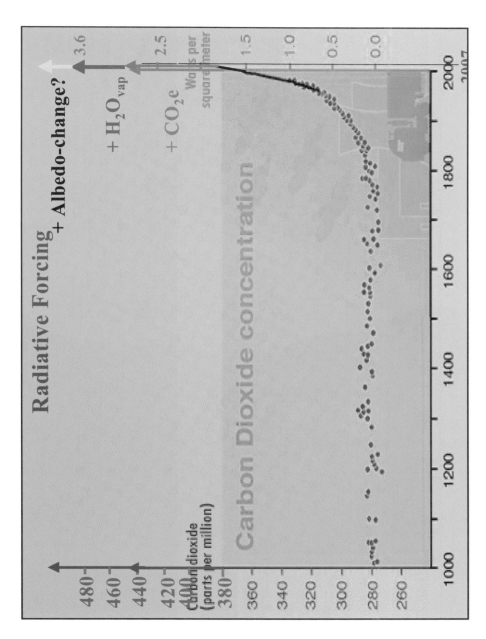

Figure 5.11

Now we add in the effect of increase in concentration of atmospheric water vapour (See Figure 5.11). Water vapour adds about 1 watt per square metre per degree rise in temperature. So our global warming of 0.7 of a degree so far, has added about 0.7 watts per square metre to the radiative forcing. In other words the water vapour feedback has added 50% to the heating due to the CO_2 we have put up there already. Then there is a small amount of change in albedo to add onto that. That gives us a total radiative forcing of about 4 watts per square metre. If we now subtract the 1 watt per square metre net cooling that I have shown you before, then we arrive at a figure of roughly 3 watts per square metre. That is the heat engine driving climate change.

If you have a reasonably large house, then if you put a 1 kilowatt fire into the attic and leave it on all the time, you get some idea of the heat energy that is driving global warming.

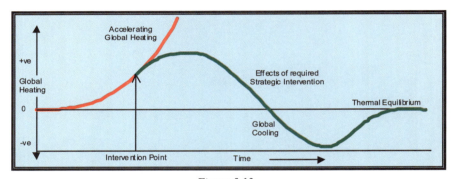

Figure 5.12

In order to stabilise the climate, we have to balance inputs and outputs in the energy equations. That means reducing radiative forcing to zero. If we have to reduce radiative forcing by the equivalent of 3 watts per square metre, what is the amount by which we will have to reduce carbon dioxide concentration in order to do that?

As a rule of thumb, a reduction of 3 watts per square metre would require a reduction of something like 160 to 180 ppm in the current concentration of atmospheric CO_2. That is what would be required to re-stabilise climate.

Radiative forcing is currently increasing at 25% per decade, and accelerating. If we made a strategic intervention at today's date, we would need to slow the rate of increase, stop it going any higher, begin to reduce the heating, turn the heat engine down and bring the radiative forcing back to zero.

Any such intervention would take time to come into effect. During that period temperature would continue to rise, activating further powerful feedbacks from increased water-vapour concentration, reduced ice albedo, release of frozen methane, continued degrade of CO_2 sinks, and release of non-anthropogenic CO_2 from burning forests. To be successful the intervention would have to take all these factors into account.

That might stabilise the climate and prevent runaway heating, but it would still involve an increased temperature. That is because the temperature of the earth would have risen to the point where it would be radiating the same amount of energy that we are receiving, but under conditions of an enhanced greenhouse effect (i.e. through a slightly thicker "duvet").

We would have prevented the Anthropocene Extinction Event, but we would certainly not have prevented dangerous climate change, and could still be facing potentially catastrophic climate change as a result of the increased temperature. The situation would be under control but hotter. If that equilibrium temperature were judged to be too hot, then we would need to go into a period of global cooling (negative radiative forcing) and reduce the output temperature to something that minimised catastrophic climate change.

In the last two years the analysis of climate dynamics has proceeded far beyond that portrayed in the latest IPCC Assessment Report. It was not taken into account in the Stern Report. The Climate Bill, currently before Parliament is based on even more out of date material, and is therefore utterly inadequate as a response to the current crisis. Acceleration of climate change is already a matter of observation. Virtually every parameter is moving faster than predicted by the international ensemble of climate models.

There now exists a state of planetary emergency

119

Questions and Discussion

Colin Challen MP (in the Chair):
Well it is like sitting through one of those all night Hammer Horror Films actually, which I did once. But that was fiction and here we have a sober factual analysis of the path we appear to be on. That leaves me rather speechless. However, we do have 10 minutes, so if you have any quick, very brief comments or questions, we probably have time for about 3 and 3 hands have come up, so a remarkable coincidence.

Question One:
Very quickly, to cut to the chase, bearing in mind, Deepak Rughani pointed out that the effects of deforestation are two fold in terms of their impact on climate change. The first is of course the deforestation due to cutting down the trees, direct human intervention. The second one, and the much larger and far more important one is the deforestation due to natural processes, but in fact human intervention causing climate change, and climate change causing further deforestation. My question is therefore for Peter Cox. He showed I think something like 8 models in order to determine what the level of CO_2 concentrations will be in the future according to these different models. My question is to what extent do any of those models take account of these two contributions from deforestation, let alone other sources of loss of sink capacity.

Question Two:
Yes at risk of being expelled from the club and having my subscription cancelled, I have to admit I have been sleeping with the enemy slightly and fallen among thieves. I have been with a number of climate change deniers recently. Many points they make and I would just like reassurance on each of them really. One is they assert, and they cite evidence which as I am not a scientist I cannot dispute, that there is no correlation between global temperatures and CO_2 emissions, that is the first point. The second point that is that, when the world was at its coolest, between 1500 – 1750 they assert there was a higher degree of CO_2 emissions at that time. I do not know whether that is true or not. The third point is, the science is so inconclusive, we should wait and see and do more research.

Question Three:
Yes I would like to ask Peter Cox whether in fact he would still stick to what he said about, to ensure 450 ppm stabilisation level a 60% cut in CO_2 by 2050 globally and continuous reductions after that actually takes into account these other feedbacks on feedbacks that have been mentioned since.

Peter Cox:
The first one was about the models. Those models actually only look at the effect of climate change on the natural carbon sinks, so they don't deal with the fact that some of that is due to deforestation, which is why I think it is doubly important that you remove that part of the driving of the system away – deal with the deforestation issue. Currently the models don't deal with the fact that the Amazon forest might be gone through direct deforestation before it is killed by the climate change. The models that we use have most of the feedbacks represented in them in some way or another, and the reason that the required CO_2 emissions cuts are as large as they are is because of this carbon cycle feedback. As far as we know they include most of the feedbacks, but not all of them. They don't include the methane feedbacks that David mentioned for example.

Question Three Supplementary:
The reason I asked is to see whether or not one could make this a policy demand to politicians, this 60% global. I think if we were to qualify, how should we qualify it in the climate change bill?

Peter Cox:
I actually think the big issue is that we don't know what a dangerous level is. We will know it as we approach it. So if we set something in stone like a 60% cut we may overshoot, or we may undershoot actually. We need some sort of adaptive policy really, the equivalent of interest rates or something. You have to have something that allows you to set a rate of change with a view to the information that is coming in. But generally speaking I think the 60% global cut obviously translates into a lot more for the higher emitting nations.

Colin Challen MP:
Perhaps one of you will deal with the issue of the link between carbon and temperature.

Peter Cox:
I could deal with this if you wish. I guess these arguments came out of the Global Warming Swindle programme on Channel 4 which has been debunked even by some of the people that were featured on the programme. The big question is, what causes what? In the Gore film, for example he shows it as a correlation and implies that there is a causality, that the CO_2 is driving the climate

change. Actually that is not true on the glacial/inter-glacial cycles, it is probably the other way round. Some climate change-driven by Milankovitch forcing affects the climate, which then affects the CO_2. And we see those effects, they are essentially the positive feedbacks that I spoke about, the positive carbon cycle feedbacks. But the CO_2 change we have had since 1750 is 10 times as large as that and cannot be accounted for by that basis. Plus it has the fingerprints of humans all over it. No-one really argues that humans are putting out 8 billion tons of carbon each year, so it seems rather strange to suggest the CO_2 rise that shows up in the atmosphere is not part of that, that it is something else and that the 8 billion tons is getting smuggled away. Also there is an isotopic signature, so we can see that it is fossil fuel carbon. That question is a kind of a done deal, but unfortunately it has been dug up again. There is a risk that we continue to devote our efforts to discussing the reality of human-induced climate change, rather than dealing with it.

Colin Challen MP:
We have got time for one last very quick question and one very quick answer.

Question Four:
If I was a climate sceptic with a hostile agenda, I would now say, 'oh I am so sorry, I underestimated the problem. I was wrong about my climate scepticism. In fact it is so serious we are already beyond the tipping point and therefore we can't do anything about it, so let's not do anything about it'. How can we show that it is not already too late, what are the arguments we can use to squash that one?

David Wasdell:
Al Gore talks about denial and despair, and you know the jokes about that I guess. When we are faced with unpalatable information we move into denial first of all. When we are faced with the facts, we move into despair. Al Gore tries to keep us this side of despair, and keep it in "de-trunk" – OK American joke. But what I have said to him is this, despair is part of the emotional work we do in engaging reality and then we go through that into the determination to make a difference whatever it costs, because survival in this situation matters. So don't be afraid of that despair, depression, mourning, grieving, reaction. Al Gore said, back in his early book 'Earth in the Balance', "if we have not grieved and shed the tears for what we have done to the Planet, we can't see clearly what to do about it". I think that is profound.

Colin Challen:
A very powerful point. I think perhaps we can finish on that. It has been an extremely stimulating session. I do hope that we will be disseminating a booklet based on this, if all of the Presenters agree to that, and that it will be distributed.

In conclusion:

Comments on the seriousness of the challenge

"Warming is accelerating GREATLY, especially recently"

Dennis Bushnell, Chief Scientist, NASA Langley Research Centre
12th Janaury 2007

"The Earth's climate is remarkably sensitive to global forcings. Positive feedbacks predominate. This allows the entire planet to be whipsawed between climate states . . Recent greenhouse gas emissions place the Earth perilously close to dramatic climate change that could run out of our control, with great dangers for humanity and other creatures."

James Hansen, Director, NASA Goddard Institute for Space Studies
18th February 2007

"We have already passed the stage of dangerous climate change. The task now is to avoid catastrophic climate change."

Professor John Holdren, President AAAS
August 2006

"The possibility of a tipping point in the Earth system as a whole which prevents the recovery of stable equilibrium and leads to a process of runaway climate change, is now the critical research agenda, requiring the concentration of global resources in a 'Manhattan Project' style engagement. All other work on impact assessment, mitigation and adaptation depends on the outcome of this overarching issue."

John Schellnhuber, Director PIK Potsdam
15th June 2006

The All Party Parliamentary Climate Change Group (APPCCG)

The APPCCG was formed in 2005 "to deliver material and meaningful progress on climate change by creating an arena in which interested and relevant parties are able to discuss and formulate policy options and encourage the application of those that offer greatest promise. In particular the group expects to:

Facilitate greater public action. While it is the role of Government to provide leadership on climate change it is the obligation of every member of society to take responsibility for tackling it. The Group will endeavour to bring the issue of climate change into the consciousness of the public fully, and to tie this awareness to an acceptance of individual responsibility.

Promote greater communication. The Group will aim to improve communication between policymakers, commentators and opinion formers to ensure a greater level of understanding between stakeholders and to provide the Government with more political 'head-room' for movement.

Encourage voluntary action. The Group will look to build Government recognition of the voluntary carbon market and to promote action beyond the regulated minima. Trailblazer individuals and organisations should receive greater support, to provide an example to others of the benefits of climate friendly practice.

Support the development of a global standard. The Group will advocate the creation of a single global standard to denote responsible and effective carbon reduction and offset. This will simplify the recognition of those that are working to address climate change, and at the same time raise the profile of the issue.

Formulate policy initiatives. The Group expects to provide practical action through the design and piloting of innovative policy alternatives such as the '25/5 Challenge', 'Contraction and Convergence', 'Domestic Tradable Quotas' and 'Carbon Neutral'. In this way the Group will have a direct and tangible impact on climate change policy in the UK."

The APPCCG has become one of the largest and most active APPG's in Westminster, with well over 100 MPs and Peers in membership and around 200 associate members drawn from business, academia and NGOs. It has completed one inquiry – "Is a cross party consensus on climate change possible or desirable?" The APPCCG has a busy meetings schedule in Parliament and has been addressed by Al Gore and Mikhail Gorbachev as well as Ministers and European Union Commissioners.

Further information on the APPCCG and how to become an associate member can be obtained from Colin Challen MP, House of Commons, LONDON SW1A 0AA or e-mail to: colinchallenmp@parliament.uk